Useful Ideas and Suggestions for Parents

Ideas y sugerencias útiles para padres

Things to Do at Home

To Practice Reading

- Read with your child every day. Educational research proves this is the most important thing parents can do to foster success in school. Establish a daily reading time for 15 to 30 minutes. Take turns reading poems aloud. Choose parts in a children's play and read the dialogue using proper tone and vocal expression. Pick a favorite song, read the lyrics aloud, and discuss the song and why your child likes it. Have your child read aloud a favorite scene from a favorite book. Discuss the scene, what it reveals about the characters, and why the author may have included it.

- Encourage your child to read the newspaper every day. Discuss the most important headline story of the day. What is the story about? Why is it the most important story of the day? How do you know? (The most important story is usually in the upper part of the page with the largest headline.) Read the comics with your child. Discuss the comic strips, the way different artists draw in different styles, and the topics the comic strips deal with.

- Start a vocabulary log for new and interesting words that you and your child come across in reading or daily activities. Look up the words in a dictionary and a thesaurus, write the words and their definitions in the log, and then try to use them twice a week. Post the log where your child can easily access it and occasionally take time to review old words as you add new words.

To Practice Writing

- Have your child write a letter to a relative or friend. Talk about the parts of a letter, such as the date, the salutation, the closing, and the address on the envelope. Discuss the importance of using complete sentences and proper punctuation. Talk about events or information your child might want to write about in the letter. Make sure your child writes thank you notes when appropriate.

- Buy a notebook or a diary for your child and encourage him or her to write in it daily. Talk about the things you might write about in a diary and why.

- If you keep a vocabulary log as suggested above, ask your child to pick a word from the log, find a picture from a magazine that illustrates the word, paste it on a piece of paper, and write a sentence about the picture using that word.

To Practice Math

- Ask your child to pretend to redo a room in the house. Ask him or her to measure the room for carpeting, check the newspaper for carpeting ads, compare prices per square foot or yard, choose affordable carpeting, and compute how much is needed and how much it will cost. Have your child do the same for repainting—determine the area of the walls, how much paint would be needed to repaint the room, and how much it would cost.

- Tell your child to plan the menu for three family dinners with a budget of $20.00. Tell him or her to check the food ads in the newspaper, add up the cost of the different items needed to fix the three meals, and determine if there will be money left over or if $20.00 is not enough.

Kids Learn!

Review Seventh Grade
Get Ready for Eighth Grade

Editor-in-Chief
Sharon Coan, M.S.Ed.

Editorial Manager
Gisela Lee, M.A.

Editor
Susan Matthewson

Assistant Editor
Katie Das

Creative Director
Lee Aucoin

Imaging
Robin Erickson
Don Tran
Kimberly Weber

Cover Artist
Lee Aucoin

Publisher
Rachelle Cracchiolo, M.S.Ed.

Teacher Created Materials
5301 Oceanus Drive
Huntington Beach, CA 92649-1030
http://www.tcmpub.com
ISBN 978-1-4258-0285-1
© 2007 Teacher Created Materials, Inc.
Reprinted 2013

Table of Contents

Cosas para hacer en casa

Para practicar la lectura

- Lea con su hijo o hija cada día. La investigación educacional demuestra que esto es la cosa más importante que los padres pueden hacer para fomentar éxito en la escuela. Establezca un tiempo diario de lectura por 15 a 30 minutos. Túrnense leyendo poemas en voz alta. Elijan partes en una obra de teatro para niños y lean el diálogo usando tono correcto y expresión vocal. Elija una canción favorita, lea la letra en voz alta y discutan la canción y por qué le gusta a su hijo. Pídale a su hijo que lea una escena favorita de un libro favorito. Discutan la escena, qué revela sobre los personajes y por qué la incluyó el autor.

- Anime a su hijo a leer el periódico cada día. Discutan el titular más importante del día. ¿De qué trata la historia? ¿Por qué es la historia la más importante del día? ¿Cómo saben? (La historia más importante usualmente está arriba de la página con el titular más grande.) Lea las historietas con su hijo. Discutan las historietas, la manera en la que artistas diferentes dibujan con estilos diferentes, y los temas que se tratan.

- Empiecen un diario de vocabulario para nuevas palabras interesantes que usted y su hijo encuentren en la lectura o en actividades diarias. Busquen esas palabras en un diccionario y un diccionario de sinónimos, escriban las palabras y sus definiciones en el diario y traten de usarlas dos veces a la semana. Ponga el diario donde su hijo pueda usarlo fácilmente y de vez en cuando tome el tiempo de repasar palabras viejas a medida que le agregue palabras nuevas.

Para practicar la escritura

- Pídale a su hijo que le escriba a un pariente, amigo o amiga. Hablen acerca de las partes de una carta como la fecha, el saludo, la terminación y la dirección en el sobre. Discutan la importancia de usar frases completas y puntuación correcta. Hablen acerca de eventos o información que su hijo quizás quisiera escribir en la carta.

- Compre una libreta o diario para su hijo y anímele a escribir diariamente. Hablen acerca de las cosas que quizás escribiría usted en un diario y por qué.

- Si usted mantiene un diario de vocabulario como es recomendado arriba, pídale a su hijo que elija una palabra, encuentre una fotografía de una revista que ilustre la palabra, la pegue en una hoja de papel y escriba una frase describiéndola.

Para practicar las matemáticas

- Pídale a su hijo que pretenda redecorar un cuarto en la casa. Pídale que mida el cuarto para alfombrarlo, consulte el periódico para anuncios de alfombrado, compare los precios por pie cuadrado o yarda, elija alfombrado económico y compute cuánto se necesita y cuánto costará. Pídale a su hijo que haga lo mismo para la pintura—que determine el área de las paredes, qué tanta pintura se necesitaría para repintar el cuarto y cuánto costaría.

- Dígale a su hijo que planee el menú para tres cenas familiares con un presupuesto de $20.00. Pídale que consulte los anuncios de comida en el periódico, sume el costo de las cosas diferentes que se necesitan para preparar las tres comidas y determine si sobrará dinero o si $20.00 no será suficiente.

Things to Do in the Community

To Practice Reading

- When in the car, ask your child to read the freeway, street, traffic, and warning signs as well as billboard advertisements. Ask your child to explain what the traffic signs mean. Discuss the billboards, the products that are being advertised, the ways in which the advertisements attract attention, and the message.

- Go to the library on a regular basis. Help your child find the types of books he or she enjoys reading. Most libraries offer children's reading events, so ask your library for a schedule of monthly events and try to attend regularly.

- Check the calendar section of your newspaper for local book events in your community. Book stores often host authors and book signing events that you can attend with your child. Other events include book festivals or charity book sales.

- When you attend a movie with your child, discuss the characters, plot, and setting. Talk about how the movie depicted the different characters and which character your child liked the most or identified with. If the movie is based on a book your child has read, compare a scene from the book with the way it is presented in the movie. How do the two scenes differ? Discuss why.

To Practice Writing

- Have your child design and write a travel brochure about his or her favorite attractions in your community.

- Have your child research the mayor of your city and write a biography of the mayor. Where did the mayor go to school, where did he or she grow up, what other jobs has the mayor had, and why did he or she decide to run for mayor? What are some projects the mayor wants to complete for your city?

- When you eat at a restaurant, ask your child to write a review of the restaurant. What type of food is served, what is the price range, what is the décor, how is the service, and is the food well prepared? Have your child describe several different menu choices and evaluate them.

To Practice Math

- When shopping with your child, point out sale items and ask your child to compute the amount of savings on an item. If an item is regularly $10.00 and is 20% off, ask your child how much you will save.

- When planning an excursion or short trip, ask your child to consult a map, plan the shortest route, and compute how many miles you will travel and how long it will take. Take note of the mileage when you leave and have your child calculate the actual mileage traveled compared to the mileage given on the map.

- Visit a bank and help your child open a bank account. Determine how much money your child will deposit, the bank's rate of interest, how much interest will be earned monthly, how much interest would be earned on an initial deposit over a year, and how the interest compounds. When monthly statements arrive, review them with your child. Alternatively, do a "pretend" bank account project with your child and allow him or her to deposit Monopoly® or play money in a shoebox, establish a rate of interest, have the child "deposit" money each month, and perform the above activities.

Cosas para hacer en la comunidad

Para practicar la lectura

- Cuando estén en el coche, pídale a su hijo que lea los letreros de la carretera, calle, tráfico y de precaución tal como los anuncios de carteleras. Pídale a su hijo que explique lo que significan los letreros. Discutan las carteleras, los productos que se anuncian y las maneras en las que atraen la atención los anuncios y el mensaje.

- Vayan a la biblioteca con frecuencia. Ayúdele a su hijo a encontrar los tipos de libros que a él o ella le guste leer. La mayoría de las bibliotecas ofrecen eventos de lectura para niños, así que pídales un horario de los eventos mensuales y traten de asistir regularmente.

- Consulte la sección de calendario de su periódico para eventos locales de libros en su comunidad. Las librerías a menudo presentan eventos a los que pueden asistir usted y su hijo donde autores firman sus libros. Otros eventos incluyen festivales de libros o ventas de libros de caridad.

- Cuando asista a una película con su hijo, discutan los personajes, trama y entorno. Hablen acerca de cómo la película representó los personajes diferentes y cuál personaje más le gustó a su hijo o con el cual más se identificó. Si la película es basada en un libro que ha leído su hijo, comparen una escena del libro y cómo es presentada en la película. ¿Cómo son diferentes? Discutan por qué.

Para practicar la escritura

- Pídale a su hijo que diseñe y escriba un folleto de viaje acerca de sus atracciones favoritas en su comunidad.

- Pídale a su hijo que investigue al alcalde de su ciudad y escriba una biografía de él o ella. ¿Dónde asistió a la escuela, dónde creció, que otros trabajos ha tenido y por qué decidió ser candidato para la posición de alcalde? ¿Qué son algunos de los proyectos que el alcalde quiere cumplir para su ciudad?

- Cuando coman en un restaurante, pídale a su hijo que escriba una crítica del restaurante. ¿Qué tipo de comida se sirve, cuál es el rango de precio, cómo es la decoración, cómo es el servicio y es bien preparada la comida? Pídale a su hijo que describa selecciones diferentes del menú y que las evalúe.

Para practicar las matemáticas

- Cuando vayan de compras usted y su hijo, muéstrele las cosas de rebaja y pídale que compute la cantidad de ahorro de una cosa. Si algo es normalmente $10.00 y tiene 20% de descuento, pregúntele a su hijo cuánto ahorrará.

- Cuando estén planeando una excursión o viaje corto, pídale a su hijo que consulte un mapa, planee la ruta más corta y compute cuántas millas viajarán y cuánto tardarán en llegar. Apunten las millas cuando partan y pídale a su hijo que calcule las millas viajadas comparadas a las millas dadas en un mapa.

- Visiten un banco y ayúdele a su hijo a abrir una cuenta bancaria. Determine cuánto dinero su hijo depositará, el interés del banco, cuánto interés se ganará mensualmente, cuánto interés se ganaría con un depósito inicial durante un año y cómo calcular el interés cumulativamente. Cuando lleguen los estados de cuenta, repáselos con su hijo. Alternativamente, haga un proyecto bancario "imaginario" con su hijo y déjele depositar dinero de juguete o imaginario en una caja de zapatos, establezca el interés, pídale que "deposite" dinero cada mes y que haga las actividades mencionadas arriba.

Introduction to Vacation Reading

The next page provides a list of recommended literature for children in grades 7 and 8. The titles listed are recommendations for vacation reading for your child. The list includes both fiction and nonfiction books so that your child will experience a wide variety of types of reading similar to what he or she experiences in the classroom.

Within this book, your child will be asked to select a book to read and to complete an activity related to that book. This list will provide some guidance in making those selections. These are only suggestions, however. If your child chooses other reading material, that is fine. Children will be more likely to read what they have chosen themselves.

Visits to your local library so your child can choose books to read will prove invaluable in helping your child maintain the gains in reading that have been made over the past year. Make sure your child chooses books that are at a reading level that is comfortable for him or her. If the books on this list seem too hard or too easy for your child, ask the librarian for guidance in choosing books that are leveled appropriately.

Most of all, make sure your child has chosen books that are interesting to him or her. Vacation reading should be fun!

Introducción a la lectura de las vacaciones

La siguiente página proporciona una lista de literatura recomendada para niños en 7° y 8° grado. Los títulos enumerados son sugerencias de literatura para las vacaciones. La lista comprende tanto libros de ficción como de no ficción para que su hijo o hija experimente con una amplia variedad de tipos de lectura, similar a la que se le ofrece en el salón de clase.

Dentro de este libro, su hijo deberá seleccionar un libro para leer y completar una actividad relacionada. Esta lista sirve como guía para elegir una lectura, sin embargo, se trata sólo de sugerencias. Si su hijo prefiere otro material de lectura, está bien. Es más probable que los niños lean lo que han elegido por sí mismos.

Visiten la biblioteca local para que su hijo pueda elegir libros. La lectura es una ayuda invaluable para ayudarlo a mantener los avances logrados durante el año anterior. Asegúrese de que su hijo elija libros con un nivel de lectura con el que se sienta cómodo. Si los libros de la lista resultan muy difíciles o muy fáciles para su hijo, pídale al bibliotecario que les ayude a elegir libros del nivel correcto.

Lo más importante, es asegurar de que su hijo haya elegido libros que sean de su interés. ¡La lectura durante las vacaciones debe de ser divertida!

Suggested Vacation Reading

These books are recommended for students in grades 7 and 8. Most, if not all, of these books are available at your local library or bookstore.

Estos libros son recomendados para estudiantes en 7° y 8° grado. La mayoría, si no todos estos libros están disponibles en su biblioteca o librería local.

Grade 7

Author	Title
Card, Orson Scott	*Ender's Game*
Alvarez, Julia	*Don't Look Behind You*
Frank, Anne	*Diary of a Young Girl*
George, Jean Craighead	*My Side of the Mountain*
Hinton, S. E.	*Rumble Fish*
Houston, James	*Farewell to Manzanar*
L'Engle, Madeline	*A Wrinkle in Time*
Lipsyte, Robert	*One Fat Summer*
Lowery, Lois	*The Giver*
O'Dell, Scott	*Island of the Blue Dolphins*
Richter, Conrad	*A Light in the Forest*
Spinelli, Jerry	*Crash*

Grade 8

Author	Title
Golding, William	*Lord of the Flies*
Gray, Elizabeth Janet	*Adam of the Road*
Hinton, S. E.	*The Outsiders*
Knowles, John	*A Separate Peace*
Lee, Harper	*To Kill a Mockingbird*
Lowery, Lois	*Messenger*
Potok, Chaim	*The Chosen*
Salinger, J. D.	*Catcher in the Rye*
Speare, Elizabeth	*Witch of Blackbird Pond*
Verne, Jules	*20,000 Leagues Under the Sea*
Walker, Alice	*The Color Purple*
Wiesel, Elie	*Night*

Reading Log

Help your child complete this reading log to keep track of his or her vacation reading.

Ayude a su hijo a completar este registro de lectura para llevar la cuenta de su lectura durante las vacaciones.

Date	Title	Number of Pages	Author

Websites for Parents and Kids

- Fact Monster

  http://www.factmonster.com/

  Atlas, almanacs, dictionary, thesaurus, world, U.S., people, and more

- Edupuppy

  http://www.edupuppy.com/index.htm

  Large database of pre-screened sites appropriate for kids and their families

- Children's Book Council

  http://www.cbcbooks.org/

  Tips for reading to young children and reading activities

- Book Adventure

  http://www.bookadventure.com/

  Book quizzes for many of the books found on the California Reading List

- Read, Write, Think

  http://www.readwritethink.org/materials/in_the_bag/index.html

  Student materials that support literacy learning in the K–12 classroom

- Kidsource

  http://www.kidsource.com

  Activities for children from infancy to age 10

- Reading Rockets

  http://www.readingrockets.org/series.php

  Information, activities, and advice for parents

- ¡Colorín Colorado!

  http://www.colorincolorado.org/

  Information, activities, and advice for parents and educators of Spanish-speaking students

- Reading is Fundamental

  http://www.rif.org/parents/

  Ideas for parents to encourage reading at home

- Bookhive

  http://www.bookhive.org/

  Book reviews and recommendations

- Primary Computer Games

  http://www.primarygames.com

  Educational computer games for elementary children

- Helping Your Child Learn Math

  http://www.ed.gov/pubs/parents/Math/index.html

  Math activities to do at home, at the grocery store, on the road, etc.

- Math Games

  http://www.mathplayground.com/index.html

  Math games for students in grades K–6

- Ask Dr. Math

  http://mathforum.org/dr.math/

  Question and answer service for math students and parents

- PBS Early Math

  http://www.pbs.org/parents/earlymath/grades_flash.html

  Math-based activities and developmental milestones for children from 6 to 9 years old

- Aunty Math

  http://www.dupagechildrensmuseum.org/aunty

  Real-life problem solving challenges appropriate for grades K–5

- Cool Math for Kids

  http://www.coolmath4kids.com/

  Math games, puzzles, calculators, etc.

- Figure This! Math Challenges for Families

  http://www.figurethis.org

  Math problems to challenge families

- A+ Math

  http://www.aplusmath.com/Flashcards/

  Math flash cards for addition, subtraction, multiplication, and division

Spanish Websites for Students and Parents
Sitios web en español para los estudiantes y los padres

- *Mundo Latino*

  http://www.mundolatino.org/rinconcito

  Base de datos extensivo para personas que hablan español a nivel mundial con enlaces a todos los temas, de juegos educativos y revistas en la red

- *EduHound Español*

  http://www.eduhound.com/espanol/

  Base de datos al día de más de 30,000 enlaces educativos en todos los temas

- *StoryPlace*

  http://www.storyplace.org/sp/storyplace.asp

  Lo último el la biblioteca digital de los niños. Explore estas páginas llenas de cuentos para niños, jóvenes y adultos

- *¡Colorín Colorado!*

  http://www.colorincolorado.org/

  Información, actividades y consejos para padres y maestros de estudiantes que hablan español

Reading Fluency

Reading fluency is the ability to read with accuracy and speed, as well as with proper expression.

Accuracy is the number of words that are read correctly. Accuracy develops as a result of many opportunities to practice reading with a considerable amount of success. Therefore, your child should read and reread text that contains mostly words he or she can read or decode easily. If your child misreads more than one out of every 10 words, the text is probably too difficult for him or her, even if assistance is provided.

Reading rate or speed is the rate at which a student can read a given text. Non-fluent readers will read slowly and deliberately, whereas fluent readers will read quickly and easily. One way to determine your child's reading rate is to calculate the number of words he or she can read correctly in one minute.

To determine your child's reading rate,

1. Select reading materials at the right level for your child.
2. Ask your child to read aloud for exactly one minute.
3. On a separate sheet of paper, make a note of any words your child misreads.
4. Count the total number of correct words your child reads in one minute.
5. The result is your child's reading rate or the number of words read correctly per minute (WPM).

The table shows the grade-level benchmarks for reading rate.

Reading Fluency Chart

Grade	Reading Rate
1st	60 wpm
2nd	90 wpm
3rd	115 wpm
4th	130 wpm
5th	145 wpm
6th	160 wpm
7th+	170 wpm

Fluidez en la lectura

La fluidez en la lectura es la habilidad de leer con precisión y velocidad, utilizando además la entonación correcta.

La precisión es la cantidad de palabras leídas correctamente. Se desarrolla como resultado de muchas oportunidades de práctica de lectura con un grado considerable de éxito. Por lo tanto, su hijo o hija debe leer una y otra vez aquellos textos que contengan principalmente palabras que puede leer o descifrar fácilmente. Si su hijo se equivoca más de una vez cada 10 palabras, posiblemente el texto sea demasiado difícil, incluso si se le brinda asistencia.

La velocidad de lectura es la velocidad con la cual el estudiante puede leer un texto dado. Los lectores que no tienen fluidez leerán de forma lenta y deliberada, mientras que los lectores con fluidez leerán rápidamente y fácilmente. Una manera de determinar la velocidad de lectura de su hijo es calcular la cantidad de palabras que lee correctamente en un minuto.

Para determinar la velocidad de lectura,

1. Seleccione material de lectura del nivel correcto para su hijo.
2. Pídale a su hijo que lea en voz alta exactamente por un minuto.
3. En una hoja aparte, anote cuantas palabras lee mal.
4. Cuente el total de palabras correctas que su hijo lee en un minuto.
5. El resultado es la velocidad de lectura o la cantidad de palabras leídas correctamente por minuto (PPM).

La siguiente tabla muestra la velocidad de lectura esperada para cada grado.

Tabla de fluidez en la lectura

Grado	Velocidad de lectura
1°	60 ppm
2°	90 ppm
3°	115 ppm
4°	130 ppm
5°	145 ppm
6°	160 ppm
7°+	170 ppm

Strategies for Fluency Practice

Read Alouds

To read fluently, your child must first hear what fluent reading sounds like. One of the best ways for you to help your child become a more fluent reader is to read aloud to him or her often and with great expression. Carefully choose the books you read to your child. Make sure you select a wide variety of genres, including fiction, nonfiction, poetry, nursery rhymes, and folk and fairy tales. Also, read books that will spark your child's interest and draw him or her into the reading experience.

Model Reading

Have your child select a book on his or her reading level. First read aloud to your child, providing him or her with a model of fluent reading, while he or she follows along in the book. Then your child should read aloud the same book while you provide assistance and encouragement.

Choral Reading

Select a book on your child's reading level. Read aloud to your child and invite him or her to join in as he or she recognizes the words. Continue to read and reread the book, encouraging your child to read along with you. Your child should read the book with you several times. After the third or fourth reading, your child should be able to read the text independently.

Estrategias para practicar la fluidez

Lectura en voz alta

Para poder leer con fluidez, los niños deben antes escuchar cómo es una lectura fluida. Una de las mejores maneras en que puede ayudarles a leer con más fluidez es leer en voz alta a menudo y con gran entonación. Elija cuidadosamente los libros que leerá su hijo. Asegúrese de elegir una amplia variedad de géneros, donde se incluya la ficción, no ficción, poesía, versos infantiles y cuentos folclóricos y de hadas. También lea libros que despierten el interés de su hijo y lo atraigan a la experiencia de la lectura.

Lectura modelo

Haga que su hijo elija un libro en su nivel de lectura. Primero léaselo en voz alta, a modo de modelo de lectura fluida, mientras su hijo le sigue en el libro. Después, su hijo debe leer en voz alta el mismo libro, con su ayuda y aliento.

Lectura al mismo tiempo

Elija un libro del nivel de lectura de su hijo. Léaselo en voz alta e invite a su hijo a unírsele a medida que reconoce las palabras. Continúe leyendo el libro una y otra vez, alentando a su hijo a leer con usted. Su hijo tendrá que leer el libro con usted varias veces. Después de la tercera o cuarta vez, su hijo debe poder leer el texto de manera independiente.

Glossary

A

absolute value: the value of a number without regard to its sign

acute triangle: a triangle with all three angles less than 90 degrees

algebraic expression: a statement made up of numbers, variables, and signs of operation

alliteration: the repetition of beginning consonant sounds in words

antonym: a word that has an opposite meaning to another word

assonance: the repetition of vowel sounds in words

B

bar graph: a chart with bars whose lengths are proportional to the quantities measured

bisect: to cut something in half

C

composite number: a number that is a multiple of at least two numbers other than itself and 1

consonance: the repetition of vowel sounds anywhere in words

couplet: a two-line stanza

D

decimals: the numbers in the base 10 number system

degree: $\frac{1}{360}$ of a full rotation (there are 360 degrees in a circle); unit of measure of an angle

denominator: the number written below the line in a fraction

dependent clause: a clause that cannot stand alone as a complete sentence

diameter: the distance through the center of a circle from one side to the other

diction: a writer's choice of words

difference: the amount that remains after one quantity is subtracted from another

E

equation: a number sentence that shows two values that are equal

equilateral triangle: a triangle with three equal sides and three equal angles, each 60 degrees

equivalent: having the same value or showing equality

exclamation: an expression of surprise or sudden feeling

exponent: a smaller number written above and to the right of a number that indicates the operation of repeated multiplication

F

fact: something said to be true; a truth known by actual experience or observation

factor: one of two or more algebraic expressions that are multiplied together

fiction: stories written from the imagination; not true

figurative language: language that uses figures of speech and cannot be taken literally

free verse: poems that do not follow a specified rhyme scheme or pattern

H

hexagon: a polygon with six sides

hyperbole: exaggeration; exaggerated speech

hypotenuse: the longest side of a right triangle; the side opposite the right angle in a right triangle

I

idiom: an expression whose meaning cannot be inferred from the meanings of the words that make it up; jargon, regional speech, or dialect used by a group of people

imagery: mental pictures created in the mind by vivid or figurative language

inverse: in math, containing terms of which an increase in one results in a decrease in another

isosceles triangle: a triangle with two equal sides and two equal angles

Glossary *(cont.)*

M

mean: average, arithmetic mean

median: the middle value in a distribution, above and below which lie an equal number of values

metaphor: a comparison of two things without using "like" or "as"

meter: the pattern of stressed and unstressed syllables in lines of poetry

N

narrative: writing that tells a story

nonfiction: true accounts of an object or event in book or story form

number line: a line on which every point represents a real number

numerator: the part of a fraction that appears above the line and that indicates the number of equal parts to be considered

O

obtuse triangle: a triangle with one angle greater than 90 degrees

octagon: a polygon with 8 sides

onomatopoeia: the use of words that sound like the objects or actions they describe

oxymoron: a phrase that combines two seemingly contradictory elements

P

power: a number that indicates the operation of repeated multiplication

preposition: a word put before a noun or pronoun to show how it is related to another word

prime number: a number that is only divisible by one and itself

product: the result of two numbers being multiplied

proportion: an equation of fractions in the form $\frac{a}{b} = \frac{c}{d}$

Q

quadrilateral: a polygon with four sides

quotient: the answer to a division problem

R

rectangle: a quadrilateral with four 90-degree angles

rhyme scheme: a pattern of accented and unaccented syllables

S

segment: the union of a point, A, and a point, B, and all the points in a line between them

set: a well-defined group of objects

simile: a comparison of two things using "like" or "as"

solid: a three-dimensional object that completely encloses a volume of space

stanza: a number of lines that divide a poem into sections

stress: in poetry and literature, the emphasis given to a word or syllable

symbol: an object, person, action, or situation that signifies more than itself

T

tone: the writer's attitude toward a subject

topic sentence: a sentence that expresses the essential idea of a paragraph or larger section, usually appearing at the beginning

transversal: a line that intersects two other lines

triangle: a three-sided polygon

V

variable: a symbol or letter representing an unknown member of a set; in algebra, it stands for a value

vertex: the point on an angle where the two sides intersect

volume: the amount of space within a three-dimensional shape, measured in cubic units

Glosario

A

agudo, triángulo: un triángulo donde cada uno de sus ángulos miden menos de 90 grados

aliteración: la repetición de sonidos de consonantes al principio de palabras

antónimo: una palabra que tiene un significado opuesto a otra palabra

asonancia: la repetición de sonidos de vocales en una palabra

B

bisecar: cortar algo a la mitad

C

cláusula dependiente: una cláusula que no puede estar sola como una frase completa

cociente: la respuesta a un problema de división

composito: número que es un múltiplo de por lo menos dos números más sí mismo y uno

conjunto: un grupo de objetos bien definido

consonancia: la repetición de sonidos de vocales en cualquier lugar en una palabra

cuadrilátero: un polígono con cuatro lados

D

decimales: los números en sistema de base 10

denominador: el número escrito abajo de la línea en una fracción

diámetro: el segmento de línea juntando dos puntos en un círculo y atravesando el centro

dicción: la elección de palabras de un autor o autora

diferencia: la cantidad que queda después de que un número se resta de otro

E

ecuación: una oración numérica que muestra que dos valores son iguales

énfasis: en la poesía y literatura, el énfasis dado a una palabra o sílaba

equilátero, triángulo: un triángulo con tres lados y ángulos iguales, cada uno 60 grados

equivalente: tener el mismo valor o mostrar igualdad

esquema de rimas: un patrón de sílabas con y sin énfasis

estrofa: un número de líneas que dividen un poema en secciones

exclamación: una expresión de sorpresa o sentimiento repentino

exponente: un número que indica la operación de multiplicación repetida

F

factor: una de dos o más expresiones algebraicas que son multiplicadas

ficción: historias escritas de la imaginación; no verdadero

G

gráfica de barras: una tabla con barras cuyas longitudes son proporcionales a las cantidades medidas

H

hecho: una declaración que se puede probar y que todos aceptan como la verdad

hexágono: un polígono con seis lados

hipérbole: exageración; habla exagerada

hipotenusa: el lado más largo de un triángulo recto; el lado opuesto el ángulo recto en un triángulo recto

I

imágenes: fotografías mentales creadas en la mente por lenguaje vívido o figurativo

inverso: en las matemáticas, que contiene términos de los cuales un aumento en uno resulta en la disminución del otro

isóceles, triángulo: un triángulo con dos lados iguales y dos ángulos iguales

Glosario *(cont.)*

L

lenguaje figurativo: lenguaje que usa figuras de habla y que no se puede entender literalmente

línea numérica: una línea en la cual cada punto representa un número

M

mediana: el valor de en medio en una distribución, arriba y abajo de la cual hay un número igual de valores

metáfora: una comparación de dos cosas sin usar "como"

metro: el patrón de sílabas con y sin énfasis en líneas de poesía

modismo: una expresión cuyo significado no se puede inferir de los significados de las palabras que la componen; jerga, habla de una región o dialecto usado por un grupo de gente

N

narrativa: escritura que cuenta una historia

no ficción: cuentos verdaderos de un objeto o evento en la forma de un libro o historia

numerador: el número escrito arriba de la línea en una fracción

número primo: un número que es divisible por uno y sí mismo

O

obtuso triángulo: un triángulo con un ángulo más grande que 90 grados

octágono: un polígono con 8 lados

onomatopeya: el uso de palabras que suenan como los objetos o acciones que describen

oración tópica: una oración o frase que expresa la idea esencial de un párrafo o sección más grande, usualmente al principio

oxímoron: una frase que combina dos elementos supuestamente contradictorios

P

pareado: una estrofa de dos líneas

potencia: un número que indica la operación de una multiplicación repetida

preposición: una palabra puesta antes de un sustantivo o pronombre para mostrar como se relaciona con otra palabra

producto: el resultado de dos números multiplicados

promedio: media aritmética

proporción: una ecuación de fracciones en la forma *a/b=c/d*

R

rectángulo: un cuadrilátero con 4 ángulos de 90 grados

S

segmento: la unión de un punto, A y un punto, B y todos los puntos entre ellos

símbolo: un objeto, persona, acción o situación que significa más que sí mismo

símil: una comparación de dos cosas usando "como"

sólido: un objeto tridimensional que encierra un volumen de espacio

T

tono: la actitud de un escritor o escritora hacia un sujeto

transversal: una línea que intersecta otras dos líneas

triángulo: un polígono de tres lados

V

valor absoluto: el valor de un número sin importar su signo

variable: un símbolo usado para representar un valor

verso libre: poemas que no siguen un esquema de rima especificado o patrón

vértice: el punto en un ángulo donde los lados se intersectan

volumen: medida de espacio

Tips for Using This Book

This book has been designed to provide your child practice with skills and concepts while your child is on break from school. The book is divided into six weekly units. Each week has 10 pages of language arts and math practice. At the end of each week there is a challenge project for which your child may have to use several skills and concepts. Following are some tips for using this book with your child.

- Set aside a specific time of day to work on the book. This will establish consistency. An alternative is to look for times in your day or week that are less hectic and more conducive to practicing skills.

- Emphasize completing a couple of pages each time your child works in the book, rather than an entire week's worth of activity pages at one time. Completing several pages each day helps your child continually review and practice.

- Keep all practice sessions with your child positive and constructive. If the mood becomes tense, or you and your child get frustrated, set the book aside and look for another time for your child to practice.

- Help with instructions, if necessary. If your child is having difficulty understanding what to do, work some of the problems through with him or her.

- An answer key is provided on pages 97–100 at the back of this book. Once your child has completed the desired number of pages for the day, help your child check his or her work. If possible, take time to go back and correct any problems missed. Help your child learn from his or her mistakes.

- A completion certificate is provided at the end of each week. Once your child has completed the pages for a week, complete the certificate together. Filling out the certificate validates the importance of the work he or she has done, as well as shows a goal has been met.

Consejos para usar este libro

Este libro ha sido diseñado para que su hijo o hija practique destrezas y conceptos mientras está de vacaciones de la escuela. El libro está dividido en seis unidades semanales. Cada semana tiene 10 páginas para practicar artes del lenguaje y matemáticas. Al final de cada semana, hay un proyecto de desafío en el que su hijo puede usar diversas destrezas y conceptos. A continuación ofrecemos algunos consejos para usar este libro junto con su hijo.

- Dedique una hora del día en especial para trabajar con el libro. De esta forma establecerá regularidad. Una alternativa es buscar momentos del día o la semana que sean menos ajetreados y más propicios para practicar las destrezas.

- Insista en completar un par de páginas cada vez que su hijo trabaje en el libro en lugar de hacer al mismo tiempo las actividades para toda la semana. Completar varias páginas por día ayudará a su hijo a repasar y practicar continuamente.

- Haga que las sesiones de práctica con su hijo sean positivas y constructivas. Si el estado de ánimo se pone tenso, o si usted o su hijo se sienten frustrados, deje el libro y busque otro momento para que su hijo practique.

- Ayúdelo con las instrucciones si es necesario. Si su hijo tiene problemas para entender lo que debe hacer, trabaje con él en algunos de los problemas.

- En las páginas 97–100 del libro están las respuestas. Cuando su hijo haya completado la cantidad de páginas deseada para ese día, ayúdelo a corregir su trabajo. Si es posible, dedique un momento a volver atrás y corregir los problemas en que se equivocó. Ayude a su hijo a aprender de sus errores.

- Al final de cada semana se proporciona un certificado de terminacíon. Cuando su hijo haya completado las páginas de la semana, llenen el certificado juntos. Llenar el certificado da validez a la importancia del trabajo realizado y además muestra que se ha cumplido un objetivo.

Weekly Activities for Students

Actividades semanales para estudiantes

Practicing Pronouns

Underline the pronouns that agree with their antecedents.

Subraya los pronombres que concuerdan con sus antecedentes.

1. Nobody brought (their/his or her) jacket.

2. Some of the students raised (their/his or her) hands.

3. Each of the girls took (their/her) turn.

4. Either the boys or Cindy will volunteer (their/her) time.

5. Someone left (their/his or her) gloves.

6. Neither Bob nor Jack brought (their/his) shoes.

7. Most of the kids like (their/his or her) teacher.

8. Everybody must ask (their/his or her) parents for permission.

9. Many of the teachers drove (their/his or her) cars.

10. One of the boys lost (their/his) book.

11. Somebody should raise (their/his or her) hand.

12. Nobody dropped (their/his or her) cards.

13. Bob and Jose lost (their/his) pencils.

14. Maria or Cindy brought (their/her) car.

15. Anybody who likes grammar should raise (their/his or her) hand.

Multiplying Decimals

Keys to Multiplying Decimals

- Line up the numbers. You don't need to line up the decimal points, however.
- Multiply the numbers as you would multiply whole numbers.
- Count the number of decimal places in both numbers that are being multiplied. Make sure the decimal places in the product equal the number of decimal places in the problem.

- *Alinea los números. No tienes que alinear los puntos decimales.*
- *Multiplica los números tal como multiplicarías números enteros.*
- *Cuenta el número de lugares decimales en ambos números que están siendo multiplicados. Asegúrate que los lugares decimales en el producto equivalen al número de lugares decimales en el problema.*

Multiply to solve each problem.

Multiplica para resolver cada problema.

1.	$46.98 x 2	6.	$45.03 x 13	11.	$10.50 x 0.60
2.	$1.49 x 3	7.	$17.10 x 15	12.	47.8 x 0.1
3.	$21.06 x 5	8.	0.84 x 3.15	13.	14.2 x 9.7
4.	$9.99 x 7	9.	2.08 x 0.9	14.	$5.75 x 0.24
5.	$1.57 x 34	10.	0.28 x 9.51	15.	$5.58 x 1.5

Multiplying Fractions

Multiply the fractions. Remember to write the answer in its simplest form when possible.

Multiplica las fracciones. Recuerda escribir la respuesta en su forma más simple cuando sea posible.

1. $\frac{1}{2} \times \frac{3}{4} =$

2. $\frac{2}{3} \times \frac{1}{7} =$

3. $\frac{3}{8} \times \frac{3}{5} =$

4. $\frac{1}{5} \times \frac{6}{7} =$

5. $\frac{1}{2} \times \frac{1}{3} =$

6. $\frac{2}{3} \times \frac{1}{4} =$

7. $\frac{1}{3} \times \frac{6}{7} =$

8. $\frac{4}{9} \times \frac{1}{2} =$

9. $\frac{1}{2} \times \frac{1}{2} =$

10. $\frac{1}{2} \times \frac{3}{2} =$

11. $\frac{2}{9} \times \frac{3}{4} =$

12. $\frac{3}{8} \times \frac{2}{5} =$

13. $\frac{5}{8} \times \frac{7}{9} =$

14. $\frac{1}{2} \times \frac{1}{2} \times \frac{1}{2} =$

15. $\frac{1}{2} \times \frac{1}{4} \times \frac{4}{5} =$

16. $\frac{1}{2} \times \frac{2}{3} \times \frac{3}{5} =$

17. $\frac{5}{9} \times \frac{3}{7} \times \frac{14}{15} =$

18. $\frac{6}{7} \times \frac{7}{8} \times \frac{4}{5} =$

19. $\frac{11}{15} \times \frac{10}{11} \times \frac{3}{4} =$

20. $\frac{9}{10} \times \frac{1}{4} \times \frac{8}{9} =$

21. $\frac{20}{21} \times \frac{9}{16} \times \frac{4}{5} =$

22. $\frac{3}{4} \times \frac{5}{7} \times \frac{2}{11} =$

23. $\frac{11}{12} \times \frac{3}{4} =$

24. $\frac{7}{8} \times \frac{2}{14} =$

25. $\frac{4}{15} \times \frac{5}{13} =$

26. $\frac{3}{5} \times \frac{10}{21} =$

27. $\frac{121}{300} \times \frac{10}{11} =$

28. $\frac{125}{470} \times \frac{320}{1000} =$

29. $\frac{5}{6} \times \frac{14}{15} \times \frac{2}{21} =$

30. $\frac{14}{525} \times \frac{15}{320} =$

Topic Sentences

Each topic sentence is accompanied by a set of statements below it. Some of them are relevant to the topic and some are not. Eliminate the irrelevant ones, and organize and restructure the rest into an effective paragraph. You will need another sheet of paper to do this.

Cada oración tópica se acompaña por un grupo de declaraciones abajo. Algunas son relevantes al tema y algunas no. Elimina las que son irrelevantes y organiza y reestructura las demás en un párrafo efectivo. Necesitarás otra hoja para hacerlo.

I. Given a choice, I would rather get a job than be a babysitter when I turn sixteen.

   1. I am more interested in a good paying job when I turn sixteen than I am in babysitting.

   2. I can earn more with a job than I can as a babysitter.

   3. Some of the children that I have babysat in the past have been really hard to manage.

   4. I have to consider the bad points of each type of job: kids can be brats, and the public can be rude.

   5. Opportunities for advancement are greater in the regular work force.

   6. My cousin's first job as a waitress ensured a wallet full of cash from tips.

   7. Babysitting only pays a couple of dollars an hour.

   8. To me, it's all about the money, and the work force pays better than babysitting does.

II. The school week should be reduced to four longer days per week.

   1. School is boring; it's just the same old thing every day, and there's so much homework.

   2. My teachers each think their class is the only one we students have; they give us more homework than we possibly can do.

   3. Personally, five days is just too long for me. I get burned out, and I think my teachers do, too.

   4. My dad once had a four-day a week job, working ten hours per day.

   5. We teens need more rest time since we're growing, and an extra day is all we ask.

   6. Eight school hours for four days may be a bit too long, but we'll sacrifice for a longer weekend.

   7. Teens are not adults yet, so we still need time to have fun and be with friends in a non-educational environment.

   8. A four-day school week would really benefit us kids.

Reading Comprehension: Story Elements

Read the passage and use the chart to identify the story elements. Answer the questions.

Lee el pasaje y usa la tabla para identificar los elementos de la historia. Responde a las preguntas.

Saturday is the big championship game, and the fifth-grade soccer team is ready. The team has trained hard all year—they have practiced kicking, stopping, blocking, and shooting the ball. The players have listened to their coach and have carefully followed her instructions. As a result, they remain undefeated this year and are now playing in the championship game.

Katherine and Becky are two of the team's star players. As a forward, Katherine's main job is to score, which is no problem with her powerful and accurate kick. This makes her a strong forward. Becky plays the very tough position of goalkeeper, whose job it is to block the opponent's ball from entering the goal. She is an excellent goalkeeper because she reacts quickly and is not afraid to dive and leap to block the ball. She also has a strong arm for throwing the ball to a teammate.

Katherine and Becky are sure they will win the championship game, but they are trying not to be overconfident. They continue to work hard at practice and to listen to the coach.

On game day, Katherine rushed for the ball as soon as the whistle blew. She passed the ball to Anita, who passed it to Emily, who passed it back to Katherine. Then Katherine moved her feet swiftly, dribbling the ball closer and closer to the goal. Soon she was in position—she shot for the net and scored! Her teammates leaped for joy as they cheered loudly.

The opposing team was also good, however. Katherine and Becky's fifth-grade team led by one point near the end of the second half. With less than a minute remaining in the game, the opponents had the ball. It was up to Becky to save the game. If she blocked the ball from entering the goal, her team would be the champion. But if she didn't, then the other team could win. Becky kept her eyes focused on the ball, looking left to right, right to left, ready to block. Pop! The ball was up, and Becky dove toward it with her arms stretched out. She blocked the shot! The entire team ran toward Becky. They gave each other high-fives and celebrated their victory. They had won the big championship game!

Story Elements	
Characters Who is involved? What are they like?	
Setting Where is the action taking place? When is it taking place?	
Plot What is happening in the story? What is the conflict? How is it resolved? How does the story end?	

24

Reading Comprehension: Understanding Poetry

Read the poem below and answer the questions that follow in complete sentences.

Lee el poema de abajo y contesta las preguntas que siguen con frases completas.

> ### *The Courage That My Mother Had*
>
> *The courage that my mother had*
> *Went with her, and is with her still:*
> *Rock from New England quarried;*
> *Now granite in a granite hill.*
>
> *The golden brooch my mother wore*
> *She left behind for me to wear;*
> *I have no thing I treasure more:*
> *Yet, it is something I could spare.*
>
> *Oh, if instead she'd left to me*
> *The thing she took into the grave!*
> *That courage like a rock, which she*
> *Has no more need of, and I have.*
>
> —Edna St. Vincent Millay

1. What does the author inherit from her mother?

   _____

2. How does she feel about this object?

   _____

   _____

3. What does the speaker mean by the line "Yet, it is something I could spare"?

   _____

   _____

4. What does the speaker wish she had inherited from her mother and why?

   _____

   _____

5. What qualities do you feel your parents have passed down to you? Explain in the space below.

   _____

   _____

   _____

Paragraph Building

Oh, no! You completed your paragraph assignment, but you set it on top of the pizza by accident.
When you grabbed your paper, you found that some of your words were missing. Now you will have
to add the missing parts before you turn it in. Circle your opinion on the first line, and get going!

*¡No! Terminaste tu tarea de escribir un párrafo, pero la colocaste arriba de la pizza por accidente.
Cuando recogiste tu papel, encontraste que algunas de las palabras te faltaban. Ahora tendrás que
añadir las partes faltantes antes de que la entregues. Encierra en un círculo tu opinión en la primera
línea y ¡comienza!*

Students should/should not have to wear uniforms to school.
There are four reasons why I think this.

First, _____

_____

_____

Next, _____

_____

_____

Another reason is that _____

_____

_____

Finally, I think that _____

_____

_____

And that is why I think that

_____

_____

_____

_____

_____

Algebraic Expressions

Combine the like terms to simplify each expression.

Combina los términos similares para simplificar cada expresión.

1. $3y + y = $ _____

2. $b + b = $ _____

3. $5r - 2r = $ _____

4. $3c - 4c = $ _____

5. $2/3d + 3b + d = $ _____

6. $12r^2 - 3s + r = $ _____

7. $4x - 3x + 1 = $ _____

8. $2 + 3n - 7 = $ _____

9. $9x + 2y^3 - 4y - 6x = $ _____

10. $8/2x - 9y - 6x + 12y = $ _____

Evaluate the following expressions. Let $r = 3$ and $t = 9$.

Evalúa las expresiones siguientes. Deja que r = 3 y t = 9.

11. $r/t = $ _____

12. $rt = $ _____

13. $r/3 + t/3 = $ _____

14. $r + t = $ _____

15. $t/r = $ _____

Evaluate the following expressions. Let $a = 5$, $b = -4$, and $c = 10$.

Evalúa las expresiones siguientes. Deja que a = 5, b = -4 y c = 10.

16. $ab = $ _____

17. $b + c = $ _____

18. $c/5 = $ _____

19. $c - 5 = $ _____

20. $b/c = $ _____

Poetry Practice: Understanding Conflict

Read the poem below and answer the questions that follow in complete sentences.

Lee el poema abajo y contesta las preguntas que siguen con frases completas.

The Road Not Taken

Two roads diverged in a yellow wood,
And sorry I could not travel both
And be one traveler, long I stood
And looked down one as far as I could
To where it bent in the undergrowth;

Then took the other, as just as fair,
And having perhaps the better claim,
Because it was grassy and wanted wear;
Though as for that, the passing there
Had worn them really about the same,

And both that morning equally lay
In leaves no step had trodden black.
Oh, I kept the first for another day!
Yet knowing how way leads on to way,
I doubted if I should ever come back.

I shall be telling this with a sigh
Somewhere ages and ages hence:
Two roads diverged in a wood, and I—
I took the one less traveled by,
And that has made all the difference.

—Robert Frost

---

1. What is the setting of this poem? _____

2. Who is the main character in the poem? _____

3. What problem does the character face? _____

_____

_____

_____

_____

4. What does the character decide to do? _____

_____

_____

_____

_____

5. How does the character feel about his decision? _____

_____

_____

_____

Fact and Opinion

If an Atom in My School Lunchroom Could Talk

I heard some whisperings as I walked past the lunchroom wall. I put my ear closer. I knew I must be delusional, but it seemed real enough. This one atom in the wall was whispering its shared secrets of past years. What an opportunity for me! The president of the United States had attended this school forty years ago. I might find out some interesting information about our country's leader.

What was that? My gym teacher had been a student at this very school with the president! He had been throwing food and did he get into trouble. What a character he was! This atom on the wall had seen and heard it all. This could prove to be an interesting day.

I pulled up a chair. The duration of lunch was only 20 minutes, but I wanted to make the most of it! I listened intently to information about events in this room. I quietly asked questions and received answers. Armed with information about the school, administration, faculty members, and the president; I couldn't wait to spread some gossip.

Suddenly, Mr. White, my gym teacher, placed his hand on my shoulder. He quietly leaned over and remarked about finding his secret source of information. He warned me not to discuss talking walls. He said that he wouldn't tell anyone that I thought walls talked if I didn't share the secrets that I now knew.

Lunch was over, and I walked out the cafeteria doors on my way to class. I heard Mr. White whisper to me, "Talking walls—don't forget." Somehow I knew that he was talking from experience. There was no doubt in my mind, I would keep all of these secrets to myself forever!

Can you identify the facts and opinions in the story? Write them below.

¿Puedes identificar los hechos y las opiniones en la historia? Escríbelos abajo.

Fact #1: _____

Fact #2: _____

Opinion #1: _____

Opinion #2: _____

Now think of a fact and an opinion that fit with the story and could have been included. Write them below.

Ahora piensa en un hecho y una opinión que encajen con la historia y pudieron haberse incluido. Escríbelos abajo.

Fact #1: _____

Opinion #1: _____

Challenge Project for Week 1

Challenge: Write two poems using the forms specified below. A good Internet resource for finding rhyming words is http://www.rhymezone.com. Type the word you want to find a rhyme for in the search box and a list of rhyming words appears.

Reto: Escribe dos poemas usando las formas especificadas abajo. Un recurso en la red para encontrar palabras que riman es http://www.rhymezone.com. Escribe en el cajón de búsqueda la palabra de la cual quieres encontrar otra que rime y una lista de palabras que riman aparecerá.

Directions/*Instrucciones*

1. Write a quatrain animal poem. A quatrain has four lines. Lines 2 and 4 must rhyme. Lines 1 and 3 may or may not rhyme. Rhyming lines should have about the same number of syllables. You may write one or two stanzas.

1. *Escribe un poema de animales en formato de cuarteto. Un cuarteto tiene cuatro líneas. Las líneas 2 y 4 tienen que rimar. Las líneas 1 y 3 no tienen que rimar, pero pueden. Las líneas que riman deberían de tener el mismo número de sílabas. Puedes escribir una o dos estrofas.*

2. Write a cinquain poem about a person, place, or thing. A cinquain has five lines.
    a. Line 1 is one word that tells the subject of the poem (noun).
    b. Line 2 is two words that describe the subject (adjective).
    c. Line 3 is three words that describe something the subject does (action verb).
    d. Line 4 is four words that express feeling or describe the subject further.
    e. Line 5 is one word that is a synonym for the subject or sums the poem up.

2. *Escribe un poema en formato de quintilla sobre una persona, lugar o cosa. Una quintilla tiene cinco líneas.*
    a. *Línea 1 se compone de una palabra que dice el tema del sujeto (sustantivo).*
    b. *Línea 2 se compone de dos palabras que describen el sujeto (adjetivo).*
    c. *Línea 3 se compone de tres palabras que describen algo que hace el sujeto (verbo de acción).*
    d. *Línea 4 se compone de cuatro palabras que expresan sentimiento o describen más al sujeto.*
    e. *Línea 5 se compone de una palabra que es un sinónimo para el sujeto o resume el poema.*

Example

Butterfly,
Yellow, purple,
Floating, flying, flitting,
Flirting with the flowers,
Butterfly.

Fantastic News

This is to report that

_____
(Name)

has successfully completed all the activity pages for Week 1.

Congratulations!

_____
(Date)

Vital Verbs

Verbs are vital to your sentences and narratives. It is important to choose vivid, strong verbs to create images in your readers' minds.

Los verbos son vitales a tus oraciones y narrativas. Es importante elegir verbos vívidos y fuertes para crear imágenes en las mentes de tus lectores.

As an experienced people-watcher, do you find that everyone just "walks" across the street? Absolutely not! Match an appropriate verb below with its owner. A single verb may be used more than once.

Como un observador de gente, ¿encuentras que todos simplemente cruzan la calle "caminando"? ¡Claro que no! Une cada verbo con su dueño apropiado. Los verbos se pueden usar más de una vez.

1. Elderly man	_____ skipped
2. Baby	_____ boogied
3. Boy	_____ shuffled
4. Girl	_____ scurried
5. Mother	_____ ran
6. Businessman	_____ strutted
7. Athlete	_____ crawled
8. Model	_____ marched
9. Student with boom box	_____ strolled
10. Ballerina	_____ sauntered
11. Squirrel	_____ sprinted

For each "match" above, create a descriptive sentence showing why he or she is crossing the street. Number one has been done for you as an example.

Para cada "par" arriba, crea una oración descriptiva mostrando por qué él o ella está cruzando la calle. El primero ya ha sido hecho como ejemplo.

1. The elderly man *shuffled across the street with one red rose he was bringing to his wife for their anniversary.*

2. The baby _____

3. The boy _____

4. The girl _____

5. The mother _____

6. The businessman _____

7. The athlete _____

8. The model _____

9. The student with the boom box _____

10. The ballerina _____

11. The squirrel _____

Angling Around

Complementary angles are any two angles which together measure 90°.

Los ángulos complementarios son dos ángulos que juntos miden 90°.

Complementary   **Not Complementary**

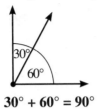   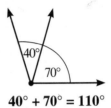

30° + 60° = 90°   **40° + 70° = 110°**

Complementary angles may be next to each other or separated.

Los ángulos complementarios pueden ser uno al lado del otro o separados.

Complementary angles never involve more or fewer than two angles.

Los ángulos complementarios nunca incluyen más o menos de dos ángulos.

Each of the two angles is referred to as the complement of each other.

Cada uno de los dos ángulos se refiere como el complemento del otro.

Label the number of degrees for each unmarked complement in the pairs of complementary angles shown below. Remember: Complementary angles add up to 90°.

Clasifica el número de grados para cada complemento no marcado en los pares de ángulos complementarios mostrados abajo. Recuerda: Los ángulos complementarios suman 90°.

1.

2.

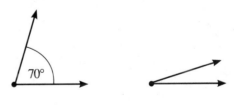

3.

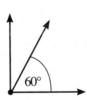

4.

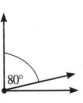

5.

6.

Dividing Fractions

Divide the fractions, whole numbers, or mixed numbers. Reduce when possible.

Divide las fracciones, números enteros o números mixtos. Reduce cuando sea posible.

1. $\frac{1}{2} \div \frac{3}{5} =$

2. $\frac{1}{3} \div \frac{3}{4} =$

3. $\frac{3}{4} \div \frac{4}{5} =$

4. $\frac{6}{7} \div \frac{1}{3} =$

5. $\frac{1}{5} \div \frac{1}{2} =$

6. $\frac{1}{2} \div \frac{1}{8} =$

7. $\frac{3}{8} \div \frac{3}{4} =$

8. $\frac{1}{4} \div \frac{1}{4} =$

9. $\frac{4}{5} \div \frac{1}{5} =$

10. $\frac{7}{9} \div \frac{1}{3} =$

11. $\frac{2}{3} \div 3 =$

12. $\frac{4}{5} \div 3 =$

13. $2 \div \frac{1}{2} =$

14. $\frac{1}{6} \div 2 =$

15. $\frac{7}{8} \div 2 =$

16. $4 \div \frac{3}{5} =$

17. $\frac{2}{3} \div 5 =$

18. $4 \div \frac{2}{3} =$

19. $8 \div \frac{4}{5} =$

20. $12 \div \frac{2}{3} =$

21. $9 \div \frac{6}{7} =$

22. $7 \div \frac{3}{4} =$

23. $10 \div \frac{5}{6} =$

24. $6 \div \frac{4}{9} =$

25. $4 \div \frac{3}{8} =$

26. $1\frac{3}{4} \div \frac{1}{4} =$

27. $8 \div 1\frac{2}{3} =$

28. $2\frac{1}{2} \div \frac{3}{4} =$

29. $1\frac{1}{2} \div \frac{1}{5} =$

30. $\frac{2}{5} \div 1\frac{1}{7} =$

31. $3\frac{1}{2} \div \frac{3}{4} =$

32. $2\frac{1}{4} \div \frac{1}{4} =$

33. $5\frac{1}{2} \div 3 =$

34. $3\frac{1}{8} \div 2\frac{1}{2} =$

35. $3\frac{3}{4} \div 3\frac{3}{4} =$

Tarzan of the Apes

An excerpt from "Chapter I: Out to Sea" by Edgar Rice Burroughs

So it was that from the second day out from Freetown John Clayton and his young wife witnessed scenes upon the deck of the Fuwalda such as they had believed were never enacted outside the covers of printed stories of the sea.

It was on the morning of the second day that the first link was forged in what was destined to form a chain of circumstances ending in a life for one then unborn such as has never been paralleled in the history of man.

Two sailors were washing down the decks of the Fuwalda, the first mate was on duty, and the captain had stopped to speak with John Clayton and Lady Alice.

The men were working backwards toward the little party who were facing away from the sailors. Closer and closer they came, until one of them was directly behind the captain. In another moment he would have passed by and this strange narrative would never have been recorded.

But just that instant the officer turned to leave Lord and Lady Greystoke, and, as he did so, tripped against the sailor and sprawled headlong upon the deck, overturning the water pail so that he was drenched in its dirty contents.

For an instant the scene was ludicrous; but only for an instant. With a volley of awful oaths, his face suffused with the scarlet of mortification and rage, the captain regained his feet, and with a terrific blow felled the sailor to the deck.

The man was small and rather old, so that the brutality of the act was thus accentuated. The other seaman, however, was neither old nor small—a huge bear of a man, with fierce black mustachios, and a great bull neck set between massive shoulders.

As he saw his mate go down he crouched, and with a low snarl, sprang upon the captain, crushing him to his knees with a single mighty blow.

Fluency Goal: Read 170 words in one minute. The highlighted word is the 170th word in the passage. See pages 12 and 13 for information on fluency.

Meta para la fluidez: Leer 170 palabras en un minuto. La palabra destacada es la palabra número 170 en la historia. Ver las páginas 12 y 13 para más información sobre la fluidez de la lectura.

What three story details did you read about in the passage? Write them below.

¿Qué tres detalles de la historia leíste en el pasaje? Escríbe los abajo.

Detail #1: _____

Detail #2: _____

Detail #3: _____

Answer the questions below by making inferences about the text.

Responde a las preguntas abajo haciendo inferencias sobre el texto.

1. Why did the captain react to his fall with such anger?

_____

2. Why did the large seaman react to the captain in the way he did?

_____

Doodling with Decimals

Write the following numbers in words.

Escribe los números siguientes en palabras.

1. .9 _____
2. .306 _____
3. .042 _____
4. 6.03 _____
5. 80.7 _____

6. 234.612 _____
7. 68.0035 _____
8. .1234 _____
9. 1.234 _____
10. 12.34 _____

Change the words below into numbers.

Cambia las palabras abajo a números.

11. forty-three hundredths

_____

12. forty and three hundredths

_____

13. seventeen thousandths

_____

14. eighty-six and six tenths

_____

15. five hundred eight ten thousandths

_____

16. five and four hundredths

_____

List in order from least to greatest.

Enumera en orden del menor al mayor.

17. 12.444; 12.140; 12.404; 12,400

_____

18. 0.96; 10.96; 0.9666; 109.6

_____

19. 0.5; 0.55; 0.505; 0.055

_____

20. 5.01; 50.1; 0.51; 0.15

_____

For problems 21–23, round to the nearest whole number. For problems 24–27, round to the nearest tenth. For problems 28–30, round to the nearest hundredth.

Para los problemas 21–23, redondea al número entero más cercano. Para los problemas 24–27, redondea al décimo más cercano. Para los problemas 28–30, redondea a la centésima más cercana.

21. 3.75 _____
22. 26.8 _____
23. 21.04 _____
24. 5.62 _____
25. 0.183

26. 7.601 _____
27. 18.718 _____
28. 304.8146 _____
29. 1.059 _____
30. 27.389 _____

The Mayas

Read the passage and the questions that follow it. Circle the letter of the best answer.

Lee la selección y las preguntas que la siguen. Encierra en un círculo la mejor respuesta.

The Mayas are one of the most interesting of the advanced civilizations that had developed in the Americas before the Spanish conquerors arrived in the early 1500s. They lived in what are now the countries of Guatemala, Honduras, El Salvador, and parts of Mexico. Most of their territory was only 200 to 600 feet above sea level and was covered with dense tropical forest. At the height of the Mayan civilization, from the 300s to the 800s A.D., they may have reached a population of about 2,000,000 people.

Today many Mayan ruins still lie buried in the dense growth of the tropical jungles. Not many of their ruins have been excavated and studied, but what we have learned about them tells us a lot about how these people lived. We have learned, for example, that they knew a great deal about astronomy and had developed a complicated calendar based on their study of heavenly bodies. They had also developed an advanced form of writing and a system of arithmetic. Their architecture and art are known and admired around the world.

The Mayas were short and stocky with round heads, black hair, and brown skin. The men wore long loincloths and the women wore long straight skirts. In cold weather they added blankets to their costumes for warmth. The clothes were often painted with designs and decorated with feathers. The common people lived in log huts that were scattered throughout the countryside and came to the cities when they had business there or to attend religious festivals. They grew and ate corn, beans, squash, sweet potatoes, and chili peppers. Their only domestic animal seems to have been the turkey. They kept bees for their honey.

The Mayas built cities that were centers for religious festivals, markets, and government business, but as far as we know, no one lived there on a permanent basis. The temples, built on top of high stone pyramids, were the focus of urban activities. Only the priests mounted the steep stone steps to the tops of these pyramids; the people watched from below. The Mayas practiced human sacrifice in these temples but not to the same extent as the Aztecs who lived near what is now Mexico City.

Fluency Goal: Read 170 words in one minute. The highlighted word is the 170th word in the passage. See pages 12 and 13 for information on fluency.

Meta para la fluidez: Leer 170 palabras en un minuto. La palabra destacada es la palabra número 170 en la historia. Ver las páginas 12 y 13 para más información sobre la fluidez de la lectura.

1. This passage is mainly about . . .

    (A) the Mayan civilization from 300 to 800 A.D.
    (B) the Mayan civilization after the Spanish invasion in the 1500s A.D.
    (C) the Mayan civilization before 300 A.D.
    (D) the Mayan civilization after 900 A.D.

2. Why do you suppose the common people lived outside of the large cities?

    (E) Living in the city was too expensive.
    (F) They were not interested in either science or art.
    (G) The priests found control easier when the people were outside of the cities.
    (H) The people were afraid that they might be sacrificed in the temple.

Conflicting Options

One component of narrative writing is conflict. Conflict captures the reader's interest. Conflict is the problem or obstacle the character is trying to overcome.

Un componente de la escritura narrativa es el conflicto. El conflicto capta el interés del lector. El conflicto es el problema u obstáculo que el personaje está tratando de superar.

Give five examples of conflicts in your past—one from each category—and explain how each was resolved.

Da cinco ejemplos de conflictos en tu pasado—uno de cada categoría—y explica cómo se resolvió.

Person vs. Person

Conflict: _____

How the conflict was resolved: _____

_____

Person vs. Machine

Conflict: _____

How the conflict was resolved: _____

_____

Person vs. Nature

Conflict: _____

How the conflict was resolved: _____

_____

Person vs. Self

Conflict: _____

How the conflict was resolved: _____

_____

Person vs. Society

Conflict: _____

How the conflict was resolved: _____

_____

Choose one conflict from above and compose a personal narrative paragraph. Include the circumstances and details of the conflict and the steps you took to resolve it.

Elige un conflicto de arriba y compón un párrafo narrativo personal. Incluye las circunstancias, los detalles del conflicto y los pasos que tomaste para resolverlo.

Comma Capers

Two or more of the same part of speech (except interjections) used in a series are separated by commas to let the reader know where one item in the series ends and the next item begins.

Dos o más de la misma parte del habla (menos interjecciones) usadas en una serie son separadas por comas para dejarle saber al lector donde una cosa en la serie termina y la próxima empieza.

Examples:

Hank brought his *bat, ball,* and *glove* to the game on Sunday. (nouns)

At the track meet we will *sprint, hurdle,* and *vault* our way towards a victory. (verbs)

The *violent, steely, crashing* waves menaced the fishermen as they rowed out to sea. (adjectives)

Read the following sentences and add commas where needed.

Lee las oraciones siguientes y agrega comas donde se necesitan.

1. Mrs. Dorsey brought her Persian cat golden retriever and pet goldfish to the veterinarian.

2. The sudden dense fog created a soft gray blanket over the city.

3. If your clothing ever catches on fire, remember to stop drop and roll.

4. As we sped away on the rollercoaster, my stomach jumped bumped and heaved.

5. A bright yellow shining light glowed from the lighthouse to warn travelers at sea.

6. The tutor helped me with my biology algebra and economics homework before finals week.

Write sentences which use the following parts of speech in a series.

Escribe oraciones que usen las siguientes partes del habla en una serie.

1. Nouns: _____

_____

2. Verbs: _____

_____

3. Adjectives: _____

_____

Practicing Percents

A local community club is offering tryouts for all interested students at its middle school basketball camp. Everyone is welcome.

Un club local de la comunidad está teniendo audiciones para todos los estudiantes interesados en el campamento de basquetbol de los grados 7 y 8. Todos son bienvenidos.

Solve these word problems. The first two have been started for you.

Resuelve estos problemas de palabras. Los dos primeros han sido empezados para ti.

1. You took 20 shots in your first workout and made 12 of them. What was your shooting percentage? _____

   $20\overline{)12.00}$

2. Your best friend made 60% of the 40 shots he took. How many shots did your friend make? _____

   $\begin{array}{r} 40 \\ \times\ .60 \\ \hline \end{array}$

3. Hi Lowe shot 35 times and made 25 shots. What was his shooting percentage? _____

4. Julie Shootsalott made 34% of her 50 shots. How many shots did she make? _____

5. Swish Malone took 28 shots and made 25 of them. What was his shooting percentage? _____

6. Slammin' Sammy made 95% of his 20 shots. How many shots did he make? _____

7. Lightning Lizzy made 34 out of 36 shots taken. What was her shooting percentage? _____

8. Your team made 44 of 68 shots in its first game. What was the team shooting percentage? _____

9. Your opponents made 39 out of 61 shots. What was their shooting percentage? _____

10. In your last game, you made 16% of 25 shots taken. How many shots did you make? _____

Challenge: Compute your own shooting percentage from a game or a playground shoot-around. Indicate the number of shots taken, the number of shots made, and your shooting percentage.

Reto: Computa tu propio porcentaje de un juego o de práctica en la cancha. Indica el número de intentos, tiros hechos y tu porcentaje de tiros.

Idiomatic Expressions

An idiom is an expression that has a meaning different from the meanings of its separate words. For example, we may say, "Hold your horses," but what we really mean is "Wait, you are being impatient."

Un modismo es una expresión que tiene un significado diferente de los significados de sus palabras separadas. Por ejemplo, quizás digamos, "Hold your horses," pero lo que queremos decir es "Wait, you are being impatient."

A. In your own words, explain the idiomatic expressions below.

   En tus propias palabras, explica los modismos abajo.

  1. Are you getting cold feet?

     _____

  2. She blew her stack!

     _____

  3. It is raining cats and dogs.

     _____

  4. He is like a bull in a china shop.

     _____

  5. I'm just as fit as a fiddle.

     _____

  6. He lost his shirt on that deal.

     _____

B. Underline the idioms in each sentence. Then write the sentence with the meaning of the idiom. Make sure that the word or phrase means the same as the idiom.

   Subraya los modismos en cada frase. Luego escribe la oración con el significado del modismo. Asegúrate que la palabra nueva o frase signifique lo mismo que el modismo.

  1. The referee told the crowd to <u>pipe down</u>.

     The referee told the crowd to be quiet. _____

  2. At basketball practice, we can't get away with anything!

     _____

  3. When it comes to fighting, my dad puts his foot down.

     _____

  4. I wouldn't turn my nose up at the chance to wrestle him.

     _____

Challenge Project for Week 2

Challenge: Find out what was happening in the world on the day you were born and write a newsletter about that day. Your newsletter can be handwritten or typed. You might write an article about the most popular songs, movies, television shows, and books during the month or year you were born, an article about the newspaper headlines on the day you were born, a piece about what the weather was like, or an article about famous people who were also born on the same day as you were in earlier years.

Reto: Averigua lo que estaba pasando en el mundo el día que naciste y escribe un boletín acerca de ese día. Tu boletín puede ser escrito a mano o a máquina. Puedes escribir un artículo sobre las canciones más populares, películas, programas de televisión y libros durante el mes o año en que naciste, un artículo sobre los titulares del periódico el día que naciste, un escrito sobre qué tiempo hacía o un artículo sobre la gente famosa que también nació el mismo día en años anteriores.

Library Reference Books/*Libros de referencia de la biblioteca*

The library will have a variety of historical almanacs and yearbooks that include information about the day you were born on such topics as sports, current events, and statistics. The chronology of a year's events always appears in the next year's almanac. So, if you were born in 1995, then you will want to look in the almanac for 1996 to find out what happened in 1995.

La biblioteca tendrá una variedad de almanaques y anuarios que incluyen información sobre el día en el que naciste en temas como deportes, eventos actuales y estadísticas. La cronología de los eventos de un año siempre aparecen en el almanaque del próximo año. Así que, si naciste en 1995, quieres buscar en el almanaque por 1996 para averiguar lo que pasó en 1995.

Internet Sources/*Recursos en la red*

You can search for events during the year of your birth using any Internet search engine and typing in the year.

Another Web source is *http://www.infoplease.com* where you can enter the year of your birth in numeric form in the search blank and find events that occurred in various categories.

Another website, *http://www.dmarie.com*, allows you to type in a date for a variety of different events on a particular day including newspaper headlines, prices of grocery store items, songs, and other topics.

Puedes buscar eventos durante el año de tu nacimiento usando cualquier búsqueda de la red y escribiendo el año.

Otro recurso de la red es http://www.informationplease.com donde puedes poner el año de tu nacimiento en forma numérica en la búsqueda y encontrar eventos que ocurrieron en varias categorías.

Otro sitio web, http://www.dmarie.com, te permite escribir una fecha para una variedad de eventos diferentes en un día específico incluyendo titulares de periódicos, precios de cosas del supermercado, canciones y otros temas.

Super Job!

_____

(Name)

You did a great job on the activity pages for Week 2 of Kids Learn!

_____

(Date)

Rooting Around

A prefix is a word part added at the beginning of a root word, while a suffix is a word part added at the end of a root word. Many English words come from one Greek or Latin root word. If you know that parts of words have meanings, you can figure out the definitions of unfamiliar words.

Un prefijo es la parte de una palabra que se añade al principio de una palabra raíz mientras que un sufijo es la parte de una palabra que se añade al final de una palabra raíz. Muchas palabras de inglés vienen de una palabra raíz griega o latin. Si sabes qué partes de las palabras tienen significados, puedes averiguar las definiciones de palabras no familiares.

A. Write the root word for the following words:

Escribe la palabra raíz para las siguientes palabras.

1. lawyer_____   5. builder _____

2. impolite _____   6. powerful _____

3. teacher _____   7. dreamer _____

4. calmly_____   8. skater _____

Look below at the chart showing the meaning of the different word parts. Notice how combining those parts creates a new word.

Mira abajo la tabla mostrando el significado de las partes diferentes de las palabras. Nota cómo combinar esas partes crea una palabra nueva.

Word	Prefix	Word Root	Suffix
dismissal	dis- "apart"	-mis- "to send"	-al "action"
complicate	com- "together"	-plic- "fold"	-ate "to make"
emotion	e- "out"	-mot- "to move"	-ion "state"
incredible	in- "not"	-cred- "to believe"	-ible "capable"
composer	com- "together"	-pos- "to place"	-er "a doer"
duplex	du- "two"	-plex- "fold"	
resonance	re- "again"	-son- "to sound"	-ance "condition"

B. Find the meaning of each word by combining the meanings of its parts from the chart above. Write down your guess and check it in your dictionary. Were you right?

Encuentra el significado de cada palabra al combinar los significados de sus partes de la tabla arriba. Escribe tu adivinanza y consulta el diccionario. ¿Acertaste?

1. commotion _____

2. mission _____

3. emotional _____

4. expose _____

5. commission _____

6. exposition _____

Noun Practice

A noun is a word that names a person, place, thing, or idea: girl, Cindy, town, Sacramento, building, the White House, peace, happiness. You can see and touch people, place, and thing nouns.

Un sustantivo es una palabra que nombra una persona, lugar, cosa o idea: chica, Cindy, ciudad, Sacramento, edificio, White House, paz, felicidad. Puedes ver y tocar sustantivos de personas, lugares y cosas.

Idea nouns are invisible. They are words like freedom, hatred, and intelligence. Idea nouns seem tricky and hard to identify, but actually they're easy. Look at these words: happy, liberty, stupid. Liberty is the only noun. How can you tell? Ask yourself, "Can I have it?" You cannot have happy, but you can have happiness. You cannot have stupid, but you can have stupidity or ignorance. Use this test on idea nouns because idea nouns are "things" and you can have "things." Idea nouns are things, but they are invisible things.

Los sustantivos de ideas son invisibles. Son palabras como libertad, odio, e inteligencia. Los sustantivos de ideas parecen difíciles de identificar, pero en realidad son fáciles. Mira estas palabras: feliz, libertad, estúpido. Libertad es el único sustantivo. ¿Cómo sabes? Pregúntate a tí mismo, ¿puedo tenerlo? No puedes tener feliz, pero puedes tener felicidad. No puedes tener estúpido, pero sí puedes tener estupidez o ignorancia. Usa esta prueba con los sustantivos de ideas, porque los sustantivos de ideas son "cosas" y puedes tener "cosas." Los sustantivos de ideas son cosas, pero son cosas invisibles.

Write **N** next to the words that can be used as nouns. They may be person, place, thing, or idea nouns.

Escribe "N" al lado de las palabras que se pueden usar como sustantivos. Pueden ser sustantivos de personas, lugares o cosas.

1. desk _____

2. friendship _____

3. dream _____

4. quirky _____

5. ship _____

6. police _____

7. coward _____

8. purple _____

9. church _____

10. religion _____

11. Ms. Garcia _____

12. United States _____

13. bookmark _____

14. *Romeo and Juliet* _____

15. tears _____

16. fear _____

17. afraid _____

18. nice _____

19. cat _____

20. hatred _____

Identifying Expressions

Find the letter for the expression which matches each phrase. To answer the riddle box question, write the letter on the blank space or spaces that match the problem number.

Encuentra la letra para la expresión que concuerda con cada frase. Para contestar la pregunta del acertijo, escribe la letra en el espacio o espacios que corresponden al número del problema.

1. A number added to 6   (D) $9 - n$

2. 10 decreased by a number   (R) $18 \div n$

3. 21 plus a number   (E) $21 + n$

4. A number divided by 18   (H) $10 - n$

5. Four times a number   (N) $n + 11$

6. Four times the sum of a number and two   (A) $4n$

7. 18 divided by a number   (Y) $n - 3$

8. A number minus 3   (O) $2n$

9. A number decreased by 10   (S) $6 + n$

10. 11 more than a number   (W) $n \div 18$

11. A number subtracted from 3   (G) $3 - n$

12. A number multiplied by 2   (I) $n - 10$

13. The sum of 9 and x   (T) $4(n + 2)$

14. The quotient of 9 and a number   (K) $9 \div n$

15. The product of 9 and a number   (U) $9 \times n$

16. 9 less than n   (M) $9 + x$

17. A number subtracted from 9   (P) $n - 9$

Question: Why did the lady put lipstick on her head?

| __ | __ | __ | | __ | __ | __ | | __ | __ | __ | __ | __ | __ |
| 1 | 2 | 3 | | 4 | 5 | 1 | | 6 | 7 | 8 | 9 | 10 | 11 |

| __ | __ | | __ | __ | __ | __ | | __ | __ | | __ | __ | __ |
| 6 | 12 | | 13 | 5 | 14 | 3 | | 15 | 16 | | 2 | 3 | 7 |

| __ | __ | __ | __ . |
| 13 | 9 | 10 | 17 |

Quilting with Adjectives and Adverbs

Color the spaces with proper adjectives purple, indefinite adjectives yellow, possessive adjectives red, demonstrative adjectives green, common adjectives blue, and adverbs orange. Leave everything else uncolored.

Colorea de morado los espacios con adjetivos propios, de amarillo los adjetivos indefinidos, de rojo los adjetivos posesivos, de verde los adjetivos demostrativos, de azul los adjetivos comunes, y de anaranjado los adverbios. Deja en blanco lo demás.

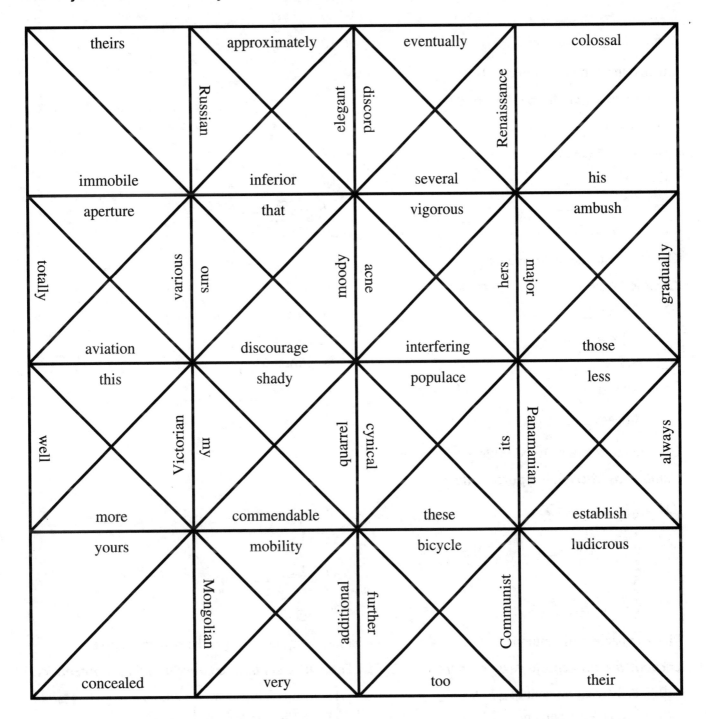

Working with Percents

Change the decimals to percents.

Cambia los decimales a porcentajes.

1. .07 = _____

2. .75 = _____

3. .035 = _____

4. $.33\frac{1}{3}$ = _____

5. .9 = _____

6. 1.5 = _____

7. .004 = _____

8. .65 = _____

9. .1 = _____

10. $.66\frac{2}{3}$ = _____

Change the percents to decimals.

Cambia los porcentajes a decimales.

11. 9% = _____

12. 35% = _____

13. 4.8% = _____

14. $22\frac{2}{9}$% = _____

15. 60% = _____

16. 125% = _____

17. .3% = _____

18. 95% = _____

19. 20% = _____

20. $33\frac{1}{3}$% = _____

Change the percents to fractions.

Cambia los porcentajes a fracciones.

21. 75% = _____

22. 40% = _____

23. 5% = _____

24. 80% = _____

25. 6% = _____

26. 9% = _____

27. 8% = _____

28. 20% = _____

29. 35% = _____

30. 86% = _____

Change the fractions to percents.

Cambia las fracciones a porcentajes.

31. $\frac{3}{8}$ = _____

32. $\frac{1}{3}$ = _____

33. $\frac{2}{5}$ = _____

34. $\frac{7}{8}$ = _____

35. $\frac{1}{5}$ = _____

36. $\frac{1}{2}$ = _____

37. $\frac{1}{8}$ = _____

38. $\frac{1}{20}$ = _____

Find the percent of a number.

Encuentra el porcentaje de un número.

39. 17 is what percent of 340? _____

40. 420 is what percent of 70? _____

41. 60 is what percent of 300? _____

Find the number when the percent is given.

Encuentra el número cuando se da el porcentaje.

42. 16 is 20% of what number? _____

43. 63 is 70% of what number? _____

44. 70 is 110% of what number? _____

Identifying Purpose and Viewpoint

Have you ever been to the zoo? What animals did you see? Have you noticed the monkeys? You should next time! Monkeys are extremely interesting animals.

Monkeys are among the most intelligent and lively animals in the world. Because of their playful nature, monkeys are very popular in zoos, where they are often people's favorite exhibit. There are many types of monkeys—about 200 in all! Most of them live in tropical areas, such as Central and South America, Africa, and Asia. Many live in tropical forests, high up in the trees. Others live in grasslands called savannas.

Monkeys vary in size, shape, and color. Some monkeys are only about six inches long, whereas the tallest monkeys can be as long as 32 inches. Monkeys that live on the ground have shorter tails than monkeys that live in trees. Monkeys also have differently shaped noses. Some have nostrils that are close together, and others have nostrils that are spread apart. Their eyes are large and face forward, which helps them find food. The number and shape of their teeth also vary. Their hair can be white, orange, brown, gray, or black.

Monkeys have long arms and legs that help them climb trees and run, and their tails help them balance and hang off trees. You may have seen monkeys in zoos swinging from branch to branch using their arms, legs, and tails. It's quite amazing how well monkeys can move from tree to tree. Some can even grab objects with their tails. Monkeys have hands with opposable thumbs and feet with opposable big toes. These opposable thumbs and toes can be used with other fingers and toes to grab even the smallest objects.

Monkeys eat a variety of foods. They usually eat flowers, fruit, grass, and leaves. Lizards, frogs, insects, and birds' eggs may also be part of their diet. Depending on the type of food they eat, the structure of their teeth differs. Those that eat mainly leaves have sharp back teeth to shred the leaves.

Most monkeys live together in social groups, with anywhere from 20 to 100 members. Some even live in family groups. Baby monkeys stay very close to their mothers, who give them food and keep them safe. Monkeys in zoos are lively and always look like they are playing and having fun. This is probably where the phrase "monkey around" came from.

Fluency Goal: Read 170 words in one minute. The highlighted word is the 170th word in the passage. See pages 12 and 13 for information on fluency.

Meta para la fluidez: Leer 170 palabras en un minuto. La palabra destacada es la palabra número 170 en la historia. Ver las páginas 12 y 13 para más información sobre la fluidez de la lectura.

On a separate sheet of paper, write short answers to the questions below.

En una hoja aparte, escribe respuestas cortas a las preguntas abajo.

1. In paragraph 2, the author writes, "Because of their playful nature, monkeys are very popular in zoos, where they are often people's favorite exhibit." Are monkeys your favorite animal? Do you think they are the author's favorite?

2. In paragraph 4, the author writes "It's quite amazing how well monkeys can move from tree to tree." Why do you think the author included this sentence? Does the author think it's amazing that monkeys can swing from tree to tree?

Before and After

A prefix is a syllable or group of syllables joined to the beginning of a word to change its meaning.

Un prefijo es una sílaba o grupo de sílabas al principio de una palabra para cambiar su significado.

tele- "far"	pit- "hole"
tract- "to draw"	uni- "one"
graph or graphy- "write"	ic- "having to do with"
tri- "three"	mis- "wrongly or bad"
pre- "before or advance"	re- "again or back"

A. Select one of the prefixes above and combine it with a root word to make a word. Write a definition for the word, and then check your spelling and definition in the dictionary.

A. Selecciona uno de los prefijos arriba y combínalo con una palabra raíz para formar una palabra. Escribe una definición para la palabra y verifica tu ortografía y la definición en el diccionario.

1. _____

2. _____

3. _____

A suffix is a syllable or group of syllables joined to the end of a word to change its meaning. Here are some common suffixes:

Un sufijo es una sílaba o grupo de sílabas al final de una palabra para cambiar su significado. He aquí algunos sufijos comunes.

-ness	-y	-less	-al	-ish	-ion
-ly	-ful	-ous	-able	-hood	-ment

B. Add a suffix to each of the words below. You may need to change the root word's spelling. Check each word in the dictionary.

B. Añade un sufijo a cada una de las palabras abajo. Quizás necesitas cambiar la ortografía de la palabra raíz. Consulta el diccionario para cada palabra.

1. kind _____   5. thought _____

2. bucket _____   6. breeze _____

3. agree _____   7. quiet _____

4. care _____   8. permanent _____

C. Now write three of your own words with suffixes:

C. Ahora escribe tres de tus propias palabras con sufijos.

1. _____   2. _____   3. _____

Expository Writing

Read the following passage and answer the questions.

Lee el siguiente y responde a las preguntas.

> Automobiles are expensive to own. After buying a car you have to have money for insurance that the law says you must have in case of an accident. Cars, even new ones, need occasional costly repairs. Even if you drive carefully, you will sometimes make mistakes and might get a ticket, which you must pay for or your license will be taken away. Even if you never get in an accident or get a ticket, you have to fill the car with gas, and prices are at an all-time high.

- Why is the topic sentence a good one? _____

- Do the supporting sentences explain the controlling idea?_____

- Are all the sentences related? _____

- Underline your choice of the following for a concluding sentence to this paragraph.

    1. Owning a car will cost the owner plenty of money.

    2. Also, you could get in trouble driving without a license.

    3. Commercials on television tell you that you must have insurance.

- Why didn't you pick either of the other two? _____

Choose one of the following topics and write a clear expository paragraph.

Elige uno de los temas siguientes y escribe un párrafo expositivo claro.

1. fast-food restaurants   4. learning a language

2. horror movies   5. a music group

3. any sport   6. any topic that you have an idea or opinion about

_____

_____

_____

_____

_____

_____

_____

Literal Equations

Some equations have no numbers, only variables. They are called literal equations. You solve them the same way you solve number equations: by getting the desired unknown variable on one side of the equal sign to discover its value. Remember to perform addition and subtraction before multiplication and division.

Algunas ecuaciones no tienen números, sólo variables. Se llaman ecuaciones literales. Puedes resolverlas de la misma manera que resuelves ecuaciones numéricas al obtener la variable(factor) desconocido deseado en un lado del signo de igual para descubrir su valor. Recuerda hacer la suma y la resta antes de la multiplicación y la división.

Example: Solve $ax - b = c$ for x.

Step 1: Add b to both sides as a step toward getting x by itself.

Step 2: Perform another inverse operation. Divide both sides by a to get x by itself.

$$ax - b = c$$
$$\underline{+b \quad +b}$$
$$ax = c + b$$

$$\frac{ax}{a} = \frac{c + b}{a}$$

$$x = \frac{c + b}{a}$$

Solve the following literal equations for the indicated variable.

Resuelve las siguientes ecuaciones literales por la variable indicada.

1. $c + d + y = b$ Solve for y. _____

2. $tx = a + b$ Solve for x. _____

3. $sm + w = p$ Solve for m. _____

4. $x - t = r$ Solve for x. _____

5. $x/b = a$ Solve for x. _____

6. $x + y = w$ Solve for x. _____

7. $dx = b$ Solve for x. _____

8. $x + b = p$ Solve for x. _____

9. $h = wx$ Solve for x. _____

10. $cy = d - a$ Solve for y. _____

11. $A = lw$ Solve for l. _____

12. $d = rt$ Solve for t. _____

13. $bx + y = z$ Solve for x. _____

14. $cr + s = t$ Solve for r. _____

15. $ab/c = d$ Solve for b. _____

16. $rs/t = v$ Solve for s. _____

Identifying Sequence

Read the paragraph. Then answer the questions about sequence. When you sequence events, you place them in the order they happen.

Lee el párrafo. Luego responde a las preguntas sobre secuencia. Cuando pones eventos en secuencias, los colocas en el orden en que ocurren.

Butterflies go through stages of development known as complete metamorphosis. This means that butterflies change a great deal during their lifetimes. Their appearance and structure change as they develop. First, butterflies lay eggs. Next, the eggs develop into larvae, or caterpillars. Every caterpillar eats a lot and grows. Then it forms a pupa, or shell-like covering. Inside the pupa, the caterpillar's structure changes, and it takes on the structures of an adult, including growing wings. Finally, the adult butterfly, or imago, forces itself out of the pupa. It gains strength as its wings become full length. It then can fly off and feed. This cycle of metamorphosis begins all over again when the adult butterfly lays eggs.

1. What is the first stage of development for a butterfly?
   A. larva
   B. egg
   C. pupa
   D. caterpillar

2. What do caterpillars do before they form a pupa?
   A. They lay eggs.
   B. They become larva.
   C. They eat and grow.
   D. They grow wings.

3. Which stage of development immediately follows the pupa stage?
   A. larval stage
   B. caterpillar stage
   C. imago stage
   D. egg stage

4. Tell the order in which the metamorphosis takes place.
   A. egg, pupa, larva, imago
   B. egg, imago, larva, pupa
   C. egg, larva, pupa, imago
   D. egg, larva, imago, pupa

Challenge Project for Week 3

Challenge: Record how much time you spend on different activities during one day for a ten-hour period, for example from 9:00 in the morning until 7:00 at night. Analyze how you spend your time during this ten-hour period, calculate percentages of time spent at various activities, and write a report about how you spent your day.

Reto: Haz un registro de cuánto tiempo gastas en diferentes actividades durante un día por un periodo de diez horas, por ejemplo de 9:00 en la mañana hasta las 7:00 de la noche. Analiza cómo gastas tu tiempo durante este periodo de diez horas, calcula porcentajes de tiempo gastado en varias actividades y escribe un reportaje sobre cómo pasaste el día.

Directions: Keep a record of at least eight activities you do during the day. Complete the instructions below to write a report about how you spent your day.

Instrucciones: Mantén un registro de por lo menos ocho actividades que haces durante el día. Completa las instrucciones abajo para escribir un reportaje de cómo pasaste el día.

1. Calculate the percentage of your day that you spent at each activity. For example, if you spent two hours in physical activity, you spent $\frac{2}{10}$ or $\frac{1}{5}$ of the day on physical activity. Convert this fraction to a percentage for each activity. Remember to reduce fractions to their lowest common denominator before calculating percentages.

1. *Calcula el porcentaje de tiempo de tu día que gastas en cada actividad. Por ejemplo, si gastas dos horas en actividad física, gastaste $\frac{2}{10}$ ó $\frac{1}{5}$ del día en actividad física. Convierte esta fracción a un porcentaje para cada actividad. Recuerda reducir las fracciones a su denominador común más bajo antes de calcular los porcentajes.*

2. Analyze how much time you spent on each activity and write a report about the way you spent your day. Did you get enough physical activity today? Experts recommend at least 60 minutes a day of aerobic physical activity for the average school-age child. How much time did you spend reading a newspaper, a book, a magazine, or other reading material? What did you read? What did you learn? What chores did you do today to help your family? Are there other chores you can think of that you might be able to do to help around the house? What was the favorite thing you did today? Show your report to your family and discuss how you spent your day.

2. *Analiza cuánto tiempo gastaste en cada actividad y escribe un reportaje sobre la manera en la que gastas el tiempo de tu día. ¿Hiciste suficiente ejercicio físico hoy? Los expertos recomiendan por lo menos 60 minutos al día de actividad física aeróbica para el niño promedio de edad escolar. ¿Cuánto tiempo gastaste leyendo un periódico, un libro, una revista u otro material de lectura? ¿Qué leíste? ¿Qué aprendiste? ¿Cuáles quehaceres hiciste hoy para ayudar a tu familia? ¿Hay otros quehaceres que podrías hacer para ayudar en casa? ¿Cuál fue la cosa favorita que hiciste hoy? Muestra tu reportaje a tu familia y discute como gastaste el tiempo de tu día.*

What a Star!

_____

(Name)

is all done with Week 3.
Great job! Keep it up!

_____

(Date)

Twenty Questions

Synonyms are words that have similar meanings. Write a synonym on the line for the bold word in each sentence. Each sentence is a clue to help solve the puzzle at the bottom of the page. Use a thesaurus as a resource.

Los sinónimos son palabras que tienen significados similares. Escribe un sinónimo en la línea para la palabra en negritas en cada oración. Cada oración es una pista para ayudar a resolver el acertijo abajo de la página. Usa un libro de sinónimos como fuente.

1. I am on American **soil**. _____

2. I'm bigger than a **car**. _____

3. I come in **concentric** pieces. _____

4. I have a five-acre **courtyard**. _____

5. The number five is **associated** with me. _____

6. I am **located** near Washington, D.C. _____

7. I am **man-made**. _____

8. I appear to be **Hellenic**. _____

9. I am **famous** for the shape I am in. _____

10. I was **finished** in 1943. _____

11. I cover 29 **continuous** acres. _____

12. G. E. Bergstrom **designed** me. _____

13. I'm the largest of my **kind**. _____

14. I hold many **secrets**. _____

15. I am **affiliated** with the government. _____

16. I have five **chiefs**. _____

17. **Corridors** connect me together. _____

18. I am spelled with **only** eight letters. _____

19. I am a **place**. _____

20. **National** news is shared in front of me. _____

Bonus: What am I ? _____

Collecting and Working with Data

1. The record sheet below shows the results of a study of 20 ladybugs with the number of dots on the outer wings of each ladybug recorded.

1. *La hoja de registros abajo muestra los resultados de un estudio de 20 catarinas con el número de puntos en las alas externales de cada catarina registrada.*

Record Sheet for Ladybug Dots

(9, 13, 0, 13, 11, 9, 0, 13, 13, 7, 2, 13, 9, 7, 2, 13, 9, 14, 13, 13)

Complete this frequency table for Ladybug Dots using the information from the record sheet.

Completa esta tabla de frecuencia para "Ladybug Dots" usando la información de la hoja de registros.

Dots	0	1	2	3	4	5	6	7	8	9	10	11	12	13	14
Frequency															

2. Teresa looked all over the house for loose change. She checked under sofas, on the floor, in drawers, and in similar places. Look at her tally sheet below. Then use the table on the right to organize her data.

2. *Teresa buscó en todos lados de su casa por cambio. Buscó debajo de los sofás, en el suelo, en cajones y en lugares similares. Mira la "Tally Sheet." Luego usa la tabla a la derecha para organizar su información.*

Tally Sheet of Loose Coins	
Pennies	卌 卌 卌 卌 III
Nickels	卌 IIII
Dimes	卌 卌 卌
Quarters	IIII
Half-dollars	

Table of Loose Coins	Frequency
Pennies	
Nickels	
Dimes	
Quarters	
Half-dollars	

Extension

- Take a survey of friends and family to determine their favorite television programming. Use the survey included here. Add other types of programming if you wish.

- After you have completed the tally sheet, complete a frequency table like the one above to organize your results.

- Create a tally sheet to survey your classmates on their favorite sports to watch or play. Then complete a frequency table to record your findings.

Tally Sheet	
Sports	
Drama	
Sitcoms	
Movies	
Nature/Science	
Science Fiction	
Wrestling	
Other	

Descriptive Writing

Descriptive writing uses adequate details to describe a particular topic in such a way as to appeal to readers. Descriptive writing needs a focused topic, an engaging lead, adequate supporting details, transitions, varied sentence structure and length, use of figurative language (simile, metaphor, adjectives, etc.), and a strong conclusion. Read the following description of a setting.

La escritura descriptiva usa detalles adecuados para describir un tema particular en una manera para atraer a los lectores. La escritura descriptiva necesita de un tema enfocado, una introducción captiva, detalles adecuados de apoyo, transiciones, tamaño y estructura de frases variados, uso de lenguaje figurativo (símil, metáfora, adjetivos, etc.) y una conclusión fuerte. Lee la descripción siguiente de un entorno.

Dark storm clouds roll through the sky overhead and the street empties. A gloomy grayness envelops the sky like a giant umbrella. Craaack! Thunder roars with anger and lightning dances fleetingly in the distance. The rain comes in torrents, beating, beating down on the sidewalks, streets, and houses. Faces peer out of windows, watching the dazzling show. When the clouds roll away, steam rises, drying the streets out for another round of play.

Use the following graphic organizer to record your observations of a setting. Then compose a descriptive piece of writing on a separate piece of paper.

Usa el siguiente organizador gráfico para anotar tus observaciones de un entorno. Entonces compón un escrito descriptivo en una hoja aparte.

Word or phrase to identify setting: _____

Sights	Sounds	Tastes

Touches	Smells	Emotional Reaction

58

Polygon Perimeters

Compute the perimeter of each of these irregular polygons.

Computa el perímetro de cada uno de estos polígonos irregulares.

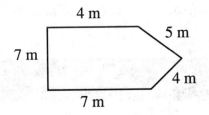

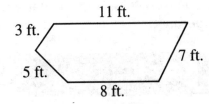

1. *P* = _____

2. *P* = _____

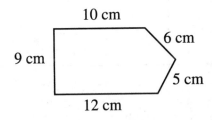

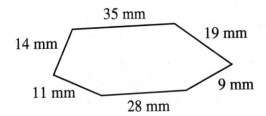

3. *P* = _____

4. *P* = _____

Compute the perimeters of these polygons. You will have to determine the missing lengths of some sides from the lengths already given.

Computa los perímetros de estos polígonos. Tendrás que determinar las medidas faltantes de algunos lados de los lados ya dados.

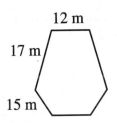

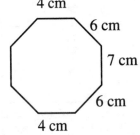

5. *P* = _____

6. *P* = _____

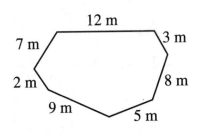

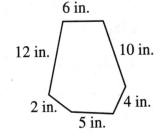

7. *P* = _____

8. *P* = _____

Geometrically Speaking

Geometry is used in math, science, and everyday life. There are many geometry terms that are useful to know. Look up the definition of each geometry term, write its definition, and then draw the figure.

La geometría se usa en las matemáticas, la ciencia y en la vida diaria. Hay muchos términos de geometría que son útiles. Busca la definición de cada término de geometría, escribe su definición y dibuja la figura.

Geometry Term	Drawing	Definition
1. angle		
2. hexagon		
3. rectangular prism		
4. perpendicular lines		
5. quadrilateral		
6. rhombus		
7. parallelogram		
8. obtuse triangle		
9. trapezoid		

Paper-Bag Puppets

Read the selection, use the information to answer the questions, and circle the correct answer.

Lee la selección. Usa la información para responder a las preguntas. Encierra en un círculo la respuesta.

This was the first day of summer camp. Katie was one of the junior counselors at the park district's summer camp. Katie's job was to help supervise the five-year-olds and to teach them arts and crafts at the recreation center. Katie and Tanya, a senior counselor, had planned on making paper-bag puppets with the kids. Katie was escorting the small kids into the craft center when she heard a loud pop and a laugh. Then she heard several pops and lots of laughter. What was going on? It didn't take Katie long to find out. Some of the older kids were blowing up her paper bags and popping them. They were having a great time, but now Katie didn't have bags for the art project. What would she do? The five-year-olds couldn't make paper-bag puppets without paper bags. That's when Katie saw the kids' lunch bags. All she needed to do was to change plans a little. She would rearrange the schedule. They would play games until lunchtime. Then they would eat their lunch, making sure to save their paper bags. After lunch, they would finally make their paper-bag puppets, using their recycled lunch bags.

Fluency Goal: Read 170 words in one minute. The highlighted word is the 170th word in the passage. See pages 12 and 13 for information on fluency.

Meta para la fluidez: Leer 170 palabras en un minuto. La palabra destacada es la palabra número 170 en la historia. Ver las páginas 12 y 13 para más información sobre la fluidez de la lectura.

1. Where does the story take place?
   A. on the playground
   B. in the daycare center
   C. at school
   D. at the recreation center

2. When does the story take place?
   A. first day of summer camp
   B. last day of school
   C. in the early fall
   D. last year

3. Who is the main character?
   A. five-year-old
   B. Katie
   C. older kids
   D. Tanya

4. What problem does Katie have?
   A. Kids popped her paper bags.
   B. She does not know how to make puppets.
   C. She has too many paper bags.
   D. The kids don't want to make puppets.

5. How is the problem solved?
   A. The kids make paper airplanes.
   B. The kids glue the paper bags back together.
   C. The kids make puppets from their lunch bags.
   D. Katie goes to the store to buy more bags.

Volume Practice

A cubic foot is one foot long, one foot wide, and one foot high. Use a ruler to measure the length, width, and height of the objects listed below to the nearest foot. Compute the volume of these objects in cubic feet.

Un pie cúbico es un pie de largo, un pie de ancho y un pie de altura. Usa una regla para medir el largo, ancho y altura de los objetos listados abajo al pie más cercano. Computa el volumen de estos objetos en pies cúbicos.

1. your patio or porch
    l = _____ ft.
    w = _____ ft.
    h = _____ ft.
    V = _____ cu. ft.

2. your backyard
    l = _____ ft.
    w = _____ ft.
    h = _____ ft.
    V = _____ cu. ft.

3. a bathroom
    l = _____ ft.
    w = _____ ft.
    h = _____ ft.
    V = _____ cu. ft.

4. your bedroom
    l = _____ ft.
    w = _____ ft.
    h = _____ ft.
    V = _____ cu. ft.

5. a kitchen
    l = _____ ft.
    w = _____ ft.
    h = _____ ft.
    V = _____ cu. ft.

6. a garage
    l = _____ ft.
    w = _____ ft.
    h = _____ ft.
    V = _____ cu. ft.

7. a storage shed
    l = _____ ft.
    w = _____ ft.
    h = _____ ft.
    V = _____ cu. ft.

8. a truck bed
    l = _____ ft.
    w = _____ ft.
    h = _____ ft.
    V = _____ cu. ft.

9. a closet
    l = _____ ft.
    w = _____ ft.
    h = _____ ft.
    V = _____ cu. ft.

Compute the volume of several other buildings, rooms, or large objects.

Computa el volumen de varios edificios, espacios u objetos grandes.

10. _____
    l = _____ ft.
    w = _____ ft.
    h = _____ ft.
    V = _____ cu. ft.

11. _____
    l = _____ ft.
    w = _____ ft.
    h = _____ ft.
    V = _____ cu. ft.

12. _____
    l = _____ ft.
    w = _____ ft.
    h = _____ ft.
    V = _____ ft.

13. _____
    l = _____ ft.
    w = _____ ft.
    h = _____ ft.
    V = _____ ft.

14. _____
    l = _____ ft.
    w = _____ ft.
    h = _____ ft.
    V = _____ ft.

15. _____
    l = _____ ft.
    w = _____ ft.
    h = _____ ft.
    V = _____ ft.

Using Context for Vocabulary

Read the sentence or paragraph. Look for the best word to use to complete the sentences. Mark the correct answer in the space provided

Lee la oración o el párrafo. Busca la mejor palabra para usar en vez del espacio. Marca la respuesta correcta en el espacio provisto.

A. The temperature was below freezing. The dog was so wet and cold that his whole body_____.

(A) cooled   (C) quivered

(B) collapsed   (D) creaked

B. It was going to be a long day. Jack decided to_____himself by eating a really good breakfast.

(F) fortify   (H) deceive

(G) weaken   (J) dilute

1. "This is really important," said Margot. "If you_____my secret, I will never be able to forgive you."

(A) ignore   (C) forget

(B) reveal   (D) explain

5. The boys were overjoyed to smell the aroma of pizza when they opened the front door. They were_____after a day without food.

(A) invigorated   (C) ravenous

(B) challenged   (D) bursting

2. The tourists in the museum all gasped in admiration. "That painting is_____!" they exclaimed.

(F) large   (H) disgusting

(G) tiny   (J) exquisite

6. Instead of allowing one exception after another, our club decided to_____the rules to fit what we really do.

(F) amend   (H) abandon

(G) enforce   (J) tell

3. The astronomer was excited as he used his new_____ for the first time to observe the comet.

(A) microscope   (C) telescope

(B) gyroscope   (D) stethoscope

7. After she spilled water on the stickers, she found that they would not_____to the pages of her album.

(A) collect   (C) press

(B) adhere   (D) detach

4. "I cannot believe that your dog ate your homework again," said the teacher. "Your story is too_____."

(F) interesting   (H) complicated

(G) implausible   (J) shocking

8. "I cannot eat cooked parsnips," said Gail. "They are the one vegetable that I really _____!"

(F) relish   (H) enjoy

(G) abhor   (J) ignore

Observation Guide

Good descriptive writing depends on using details and vivid words to excite the reader. Use this observation guide to help you learn how to collect sensory details for descriptive writing.

La escritura descriptiva buena depende de usar detalles y palabras vívidas para emocionar al lector. Usa esta guía de observación para ayudarte a aprender cómo coleccionar detalles sensoriales para una escritura descriptiva.

Choose a subject to observe and complete the following activities.

Elige un sujeto para observar y completa las actividades siguientes.

Subject being observed: _____   Date: _____

Time of day or night: _____

Purpose for observation: _____

Observe the subject carefully and record details that appeal to your senses in the chart below.

Sight	Sound	Smell	Touch	Taste

Emotional reaction to the subject: _____

Working with Bar Graphs

This single bar graph shows the number of electoral votes for each of the 10 most populated states. There are 538 electoral votes distributed among the 50 states and the District of Columbia elected by the people to officially vote for the president of the United States. It takes 270 electoral votes to win an election.

Esta gráfica de barras muestra el número de votos electorales para cada uno de los estados más poblados. Hay 538 votos electorales distribuidos entre los 50 estados y el Distrito de Columbia elegidos por la gente para votar oficialmente por el presidente de los Estados Unidos. Toma 270 votos electorales para ganar una elección.

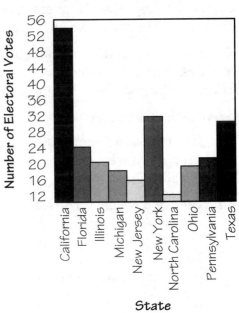

Use the information in the graph to answer these questions.

Usa la información en la gráfica para responder a estas preguntas.

1. How many electoral votes does California have? _____

2. How many electoral votes does Texas have? _____

3. What is the interval between numbers on the scale? _____

4. How many electoral votes does New Jersey have? _____

5. What is the difference in the number of votes between Michigan and Illinois? _____

6. Which state has exactly one more electoral vote than Texas? _____

7. What is the total number of electoral votes of the 10 most populated states? _____

8. How many electoral votes are distributed among the remaining 40 states and the District of Columbia? _____

9. Why would a candidate spend more time campaigning in California than in North Carolina?

   _____

10. How many more votes than these 10 states would be needed to win a presidential election?

   _____

11. Which two states combined have the same number of electoral votes as California?

   _____

12. Why did the intervals start with 12 votes? _____

13. What could be misleading about this graph? _____

Challenge Project for Week 4

Challenge: Take a survey among friends, family members, and neighbors to find out the most popular ice cream flavors. Make a bar graph of your results on the graph paper at the back of this book and write a report about what you found out.

Reto: Haz una encuesta entre amigos, parientes y vecinos para averiguar los sabores de helado más populares. Haz una gráfica de barras de tus resultados en el papel gráfico al final de este libro y escribe un reportaje de lo que encontraste.

Directions/*Instrucciones*

1. Create a survey form with choices of ice cream that you can duplicate and distribute to the people you want to survey. You can create your form by hand using paper or index cards or on the computer.

1. *Crea una encuesta con elecciones de helado que puedas duplicar y distribuir a las personas que quieres entrevistar. Puedes crear tu forma usando papel o tarjetas o en la computadora.*

2. Distribute your survey forms to at least 20 people so you will have enough data to make an interesting chart or graph.

2. *Distribuye tus formas de encuesta a por lo menos 20 personas para que tengas suficiente información para hacer una tabla o gráfica interesante.*

3. After you collect your survey forms, tabulate your results. Make a bar graph using the graph paper at the back of this book and different colors for each flavor of ice cream. Along the left side of the bar graph, you will list the number of the people surveyed from 1 to 20. Along the bottom, you will list each flavor of ice cream and then color in the graph squares to reflect the total number of people that liked each flavor best.

3. *Después de que colecciones las formas de encuesta, tabula tus resultados. Haz una gráfica de barras usando papel gráfico al final de este libro y colores diferentes para cada sabor de helado. Por el lado izquierdo de la gráfica, enumerarás el número de personas en la encuesta del 1 al 20. Por abajo, enumerarás cada sabor de helado y luego colorearás los cuadrados en la gráfica para reflejar el número total de personas que prefieren ese sabor.*

4. Write your report by hand or on the computer. Include in your report some facts about ice cream that you learned by doing research at the library or on the Internet. Check the library for the following suggested readings: *Chocolate, Strawberry, and Vanilla: A History of American Ice Cream* by Anne Funderburg, or *The Great American Ice Cream Book* by Paul Dickson. On the Internet, use a search engine and type in "ice cream history" to find Web pages about the topic.

4. *Escribe un reportaje a mano o a máquina. Incluye en tu reportaje algunos datos sobre el helado que aprendiste haciendo investigación en la biblioteca o en la red. Consulta la biblioteca por los siguientes recursos recomendados: "Chocolate, Strawberry, and Vanilla: A History of American Ice Cream" por Anne Funderburg, o "The Great American Ice Cream Book" por Paul Dickson. En la red, usa una búsqueda y escribe "ice cream history" para encontrar páginas de Web sobre el tema.*

Congratulations

This is to certify that

_____
(Name)

has successfully completed Week 4 of Kids Learn!

_____
(Date)

Super Job!

My Topic Is...

In a paragraph, the topic sentence is usually the first sentence. It's an important sentence because it tells what the paragraph will be about. Here are two topic sentences. Circle the one that sounds more interesting to you.

En un párrafo, la oración tópica usualmente es la primera oración. Es una oración importante porque dice de lo que tratará el párrafo. He aquí dos oraciones tópicas. Encierra en un círculo la que te suena interesante.

> This is about vegetables.
>
> In an ideal world, there would be no need for vegetables.

A good topic sentence not only tells what the topic will be; it also says something more about the topic or expresses a point of view.

Una oración tópica buena no sólo dice lo que será el tema; también dice algo más sobre el tema o expresa un punto de vista.

Here is a list of topics. Write an interesting topic sentence that tells what you would like to say about each topic. Write a topic sentence that will make a reader want to read more. Be creative! The first one has been completed as an example.

He aquí una lista de temas. Escribe una oración tópica interesante que diga lo que quisieras decir sobre cada tema. Escribe una oración tópica que hará que el lector quiera leer más. ¡Sé creativo! La primera ha sido hecha como ejemplo.

1. packages There is something very mysterious and exciting about a package.

2. high school _____

3. cars _____

4. sleep _____

5. carrots _____

6. sports _____

7. French fries _____

8. magazines _____

9. families _____

10. movies _____

68

Connotation and Denotation

In writing, there are two different kinds of meanings of the words you use. The denotation of a word is the meaning in the dictionary. The connotation of a word is the feeling or mental picture that people associate with the word.

En la escritura, hay dos tipos diferentes de significados de las palabras que usas. La denotación de una palabra es el significado en el diccionario. La conotación de una palabra es el sentido o dibujo mental que la gente asocia con la palabra.

For example, the words *notorious* and *famous* have different connotations. *Notorious* has a negative connotation. It makes you think that a person is well known for bad or outrageous things. *Famous* suggests that a person is well known for all the good and wonderful things he or she did.

Por ejemplo, las palabras "notorious" y "famous" tienen conotaciones diferentes. "Notorious" tiene una conotación negativa. Te hace pensar que una persona es conocida por cosas malas o extravagantes. "Famous" sugiere que una persona es conocida por las cosas buenas y maravillosas que hizo.

Think carefully about the connotations of the words you use. Connotations can have an important effect on your writing and the meanings that words convey to your reader.

Piensa con cuidado sobre las conotaciones de las palabras que usas. Las conotaciones pueden tener un efecto importante en tu escritura y los significados que las palabras transmiten a tu lector.

A. Label each of the words below, writing either *positive* or *negative* to describe its connotation.

A. Clasifica cada una de las palabras abajo, escribiendo positiva o negativa para describir su conotación.

1. _____ quickly/hastily _____
2. _____ debate/argument _____
3. _____ odor/fragrance _____
4. _____ snoop/investigate _____
5. _____ attract/lure _____
6. _____ call/yell _____

B. For each of the following words, write a word that has a similar denotation but has a different connotation. Feel free to use a thesaurus for this activity.

B. Para cada una de las palabras siguientes, escribe una palabra que tenga una denotación similar pero que tenga una conotación diferente. Puedes usar un libro de sinónimos para esta actividad.

1. mistake _____
2. revere _____
3. regretful _____
4. mend _____
5. melt _____
6. spunk _____

Using Formulas

Use the formulas for finding the radius and diameter to answer these questions. (*Remember:* $r = \frac{1}{2}d$ and $d = 2r$.)

Usa las fórmulas para encontrar el radio y el diámetro para responder a estas preguntas.

1. If a circle has a radius of 2 feet, what is its diameter? _____

2. What is the radius of this circle? _____

3. What is the diameter of this circle? _____

4. If a circle has a diameter of 17 inches, what is its radius? _____

5. If a circle has a diameter of $3\frac{1}{2}$ inches, what is its radius? _____

Use the formula for finding the circumference of this circle (C = π x *d*, where π = 3.14).

Usa la fórmula para encontrar la circunferencia de este círculo (C = π x d, donde π = 3.14).

6. What is the circumference of this circle? _____

Use the formula for finding the area of this circle ($A = \pi\, r^2$ where π = 3.14).

Usa la fórmula para encontrar el área de este círculo (A = π r2 donde π = 3.14).

7. What is the area of this circle? _____

Solving Word Problems with Geometry

The area of a flat surface is a measure of how much space is covered by that surface. Area is measured in square units. Use the following formulas to solve the problems.

El área de una superficie plana es una medida de cuánto espacio se cubre por esa superficie. El área se mide en unidades cuadradas. Usa las fórmulas siguientes para resolver los problemas.

Area of a Rectangle/**Área de un rectángulo:** A = *l* x *w* (area = length x width) or A = *b* x *h* (area = base x height)

Area of a Parallelogram/**Área de un paralelogramo:** A = *b* x *h* (area = base x height)

For this practice page, you need to know the following/**Para esta página de práctica necesitas saber lo siguiente:**

- Wallpaper is sold in double rolls totaling 44 square feet.
- Carpeting is priced by the square yard.
- There are 9 square feet in 1 square yard.
- You cannot buy partial rolls of carpeting or wallpaper.

- *Papel tapiz se vende en rollos dobles que equivalen 44 pies cuadrados.*
- *Alfombrado se le da precio por yarda cuadrada.*
- *Hay 9 pies cuadrados en 1 yarda cuadrada.*
- *No puedes comprar rollos parciales de alfombrado ni papel tapiz.*

---

1. Your mother said you can have new carpeting in your room if you compute the amount of carpeting needed and the cost. The length of your room is $18\frac{1}{2}$ feet and the width is 17 feet. The cost of one medium grade of carpeting is $20.00 per square yard.

   A. Compute the number of square feet in the room: _____

   B. Convert square feet to square yards (divide by 9): _____

   C. Compute the cost of carpeting needed (multiply by $20.00): _____

2. You want to cover one wall of your room with neon-colored wallpaper that costs $25.00 for a double roll containing 44 square feet. The wall is $18\frac{1}{2}$ feet long and 10 feet high.

   A. Compute the area of your wall in square feet. _____

   B. Determine how many rolls of wallpaper you need: _____

   C. Compute the cost of the wallpaper: _____

3. Your friend decided to paint the walls and the ceiling of her room with a lovely lavender paint. One gallon of this paint will cover only 400 square feet and costs $17.99 a gallon. These are the dimensions of her room:

   - Wall 1 — $21\frac{1}{4}$ feet long and $11\frac{1}{2}$ feet high
   - Wall 2 — 20 feet long and $11\frac{1}{2}$ feet high
   - Ceiling — $21\frac{1}{4}$ feet long and 20 feet wide
   - Wall 3 — $21\frac{1}{4}$ feet long and $11\frac{1}{2}$ feet high
   - Wall 4 — 20 feet long and $11\frac{1}{2}$ feet high

   A. Compute the area of each wall and ceiling in square feet.

      Wall 1 _____   Wall 2 _____   Wall 3 _____   Wall 4 _____   Ceiling _____

   B. Compute the total area in square feet: _____

   C. Determine how many gallons of paint are needed: _____

   D. Compute the total cost of the paint: _____

Expository Writing

Read the following example of an expository paragraph. It begins with a topic sentence that states the topic and controlling idea.

Lee el ejemplo siguiente de un párrafo expositivo. Empieza con una oración tópica que dice el tópico y la idea principal.

> *Some amusement park rides, like roller coasters, can be frightening experiences. Looking at a roller coaster from the ground can make you think it is fun. However, once you are up in the air, your feelings can change. The coaster goes higher than you thought. The cars bump and swerve around so you feel as if you are about to fall out. Going to an amusement park is enjoyable, but it might be scary, too.*

The **topic** is amusement park rides. The **controlling idea** is that rides can be a frightening experience. Developing the controlling idea with explanations and details makes a good expository paragraph.

El tema es juegos en un parque de atracciones. La idea principal es que los juegos pueden ser una experiencia aterradora. Desarrollando la idea principal con explicaciones y detalles hace un buen párrafo expositivo.

Read the following paragraph/*Lee el párrafo siguiente:*

> Mrs. Smith became one of my favorite teachers when she went out of the way to help me when I was having trouble with math. Mrs. Smith would always come in early to help me and other students who had trouble understanding their multiplication and division problems. She would often think of activities using food, such as cookies or candy, to help us learn some difficult lesson. Whenever I had trouble understanding a new idea, she would go over it again but not embarrass me. I think I am doing well in math today because of the help Mrs. Smith gave me in the fifth grade.

Answer these questions about the paragraph.

Responde a estas preguntas sobre el párrafo.

1. What is the topic?

   _____

2. What is the controlling idea?

   _____

3. What are the three main supporting ideas?

   _____

   _____

   _____

4. Do you think the concluding sentence is a good one? Why?

   _____

   _____

Identifying Cause and Effect

Fill in the following chart with the missing causes or effects. Remember that a cause is why something happens. The effect is what happens.

Llena la tabla siguiente con las causas y los efectos faltantes. Recuerda que una causa es por qué algo pasa. El efecto es lo que pasa.

One Saturday, Jeff was finishing his homework. His assignment was to write about a typical weekend at his house. He began: "Weekends around the old Jiggleman house aren't always very restful. Though the school week is over and my parents don't have to work, there is still plenty to be done. Sometimes it's just plain chaos!"

"Take today, for example. My sister is on the cheerleading squad at her school. This morning, she had to meet in the school gym for indoor practice, and my mom was supposed to give her a ride. My mom had been baking her world-famous cookies all morning for a birthday party, and I was supposed to be shoveling the snow out of the driveway. Unfortunately, I forgot to do it."

"When my sister was ready to go, she found my mom in the kitchen. My mom had forgotten about the practice. She quickly put on her coat, leaving a sheet of cookies in the oven. When she opened the garage door, she found that the driveway hadn't been shoveled. They each grabbed shovels and cleared away enough snow so that my mom could back the car out. When my mom got home, she told me that my sister was late to the practice. She also said that I had better shovel the driveway if I wanted to eat dinner."

"When she walked into the kitchen, it was full of smoke, and the smoke detector had just gone off. 'My cookies!' she shouted. After letting them cool, Mom threw the blackened cookies into the trash. Since she wasn't having a very good day, I realized that I had better do an exceptional job of shoveling."

"Since I did such a good job, my mom gave me some of her world-famous cookies. When my dad and sister came home, we all had cookies and talked about the cheerleading practice. The cheerleaders had been trying to build a pyramid. But whenever the last girl got to the top, it became too wobbly, and the whole pyramid collapsed. She said that finally, during their last attempt, they were able to build the pyramid without falling apart. We were all happy for her."

Jeff concluded his story. "Even though it's hectic sometimes, you could say that weekends are pretty enjoyable around the old Jiggleman house."

Cause—What made it happen?   **Effect**—What happened?

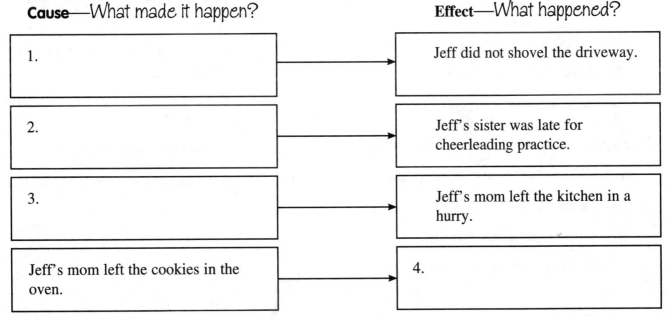

Cause	Effect
1.	Jeff did not shovel the driveway.
2.	Jeff's sister was late for cheerleading practice.
3.	Jeff's mom left the kitchen in a hurry.
Jeff's mom left the cookies in the oven.	4.

Reading Comprehension

Read the passage and circle the letter of the correct answer in the questions that follow.

Lee el pasaje y encierra en un círculo la letra de la respuesta correcta en las preguntas que siguen.

Anthropology is the study of human beings. (*Anthrop* means humans and *ology* means study of.) It is concerned with all aspects of human development. Because of this broad approach, it is generally divided into two branches: cultural anthropology and physical anthropology.

Cultural anthropology is the study of people who are alive today, and it has traditionally focused on the societies of the world which have little (or at least less) technology. It is the study of the broad area of learned behavior occurring only among humans. A cultural anthropologist making a study of an Eskimo village, for example, would study clothing, food, religious practices, and a wide range of Eskimo behaviors.

Physical anthropology is the study of the biological features of humans. Physical anthropologists trace and follow the development of the bones and skulls that they find to put together the fascinating story of human variation and human development. Their study can include people who are alive today, but often it deals with people who lived and died long ago.

Because human beings are so complex, however, it is impossible to separate completely the subject matters of these two branches. The *biocultural* approach to anthropology, which combines the physical and the cultural features, offers the best overall look at human beings.

Fluency Goal: Read 170 words in one minute. The highlighted word is the 170th word in the passage. See pages 12 and 13 for information on fluency.

Meta para la fluidez: Leer 170 palabras en un minuto. La palabra destacada es la palabra número 170 en la historia. Ver las páginas 12 y 13 para más información sobre la fluidez de la lectura.

1. What is the topic of the selection?

    (A) cultural anthropology

    (B) physical anthropology

    (C) anthropology in general

    (D) anthropologists

2. Physical anthropology is concerned with . . .

    (F) all aspects of human development.

    (G) the history of human biology.

    (H) food and religious practices.

    (J) the broad area of learned behavior.

3. The author takes the position that it is impossible to completely separate physical and cultural anthropology because . . .

    (A) both branches deal with people who are alive today.

    (B) both branches deal with people who left only bones to study.

    (C) human beings are so complex.

    (D) human beings always have a culture.

Working with Graphs

Read each question. Then look at the graph and find the best answer. Circle the letter of the correct answer.

Lee cada pregunta. Luego mira la gráfica y encuentra la mejor respuesta. Encierra en un círculo la letra de la respuesta correcta.

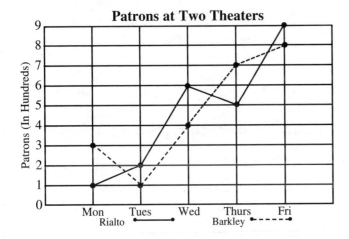

A. How many more patrons were at the Rialto than at the Barkley on Wednesday?

    (1) 100   (2) 200

    (3) 300   (4) 400

B. The graph indicates that the greatest theater attendance was on . . .

    (1) Tuesday   (2) Wednesday

    (3) Thursday (4) Friday

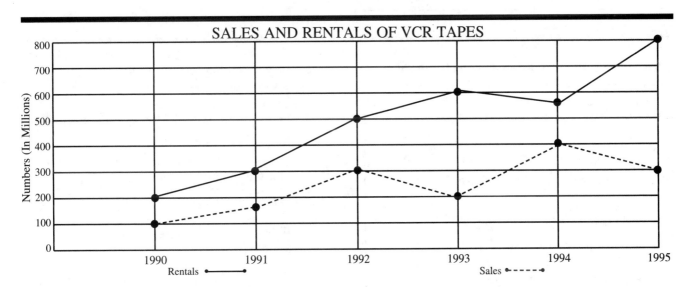

1. During which year did the rental of VCR tapes fall?

    (1) 1991   (2) 1992

    (3) 1994   (4) 1995

2. In which year were the fewest VCR tapes sold?

    (1) 1990   (2) 1991

    (3) 1992   (4) 1993

3. In which year was the difference between sales and rentals the least?

    (1) 1990   (2) 1991

    (3) 1992   (4) 1994

4. In which year was the difference between sales and rentals the greatest?

    (1) 1990   (2) 1992

    (3) 1993   (4) 1995

Using the Table of Contents

Read the question in each item. Then look at the table of contents and find the best answer. Circle the letter of the correct answer.

Lee la pregunta. Luego mira la tabla de contenido y encuentra la mejor respuesta. Encierra en un círculo la letra de la respuesta correcta.

This is the table of contents from the book *Celebrations Around the World.*

Table of Contents

Chapter		Page
1	Christmas Feasts in France	4
2	New Year's Day in Brazil	15
3	ANZAC Day in Australia	26
4	Carnival Dances in Brazil	38
5	Guy Fawkes Day in England	47
6	Sukkot in Israel	60

A. For information about Brazilian folk dances you should look in which chapter?

(1) 1   (2) 2   (3) 3   (4) 4

B. In Chapter 3 you might find out…

(1) what holidays are celebrated in England.
(2) when Carnival takes place.
(3) who Guy Fawkes was.
(4) what ANZAC means.

This is the table of contents from the book *Up in the Attic.*

Table of Contents

Chapter		Page
1	A Rainy Saturday	3
2	Meg and Barb Explore	12
3	A Mysterious Shadow	20
4	The Locked Chest	29
5	The Key in the Corner	40
6	Grandmother's Treasure	52

1. In which chapter might this sentence appear?

"Oh, it's just the tree outside the attic window," Meg gasped in relief.

(1) Chapter 1
(2) Chapter 2
(3) Chapter 3
(4) Chapter 4

2. In which chapter might you find this sentence?

"I had planned to spend the day hiking in the woods," said Meg.

(1) Chapter 1   (3) Chapter 4
(2) Chapter 2   (4) Chapter 6

3. In which chapter might these sentences appear?

"Look, Meg" Barb whispered. "What is that shiny thing over there?"

(1) Chapter 3   (3) Chapter 5
(2) Chapter 4   (4) Chapter 6

4. In which chapter might you read this?

"I think Grandmother would be happy that we found it," said Meg.

(1) Chapter 1   (3) Chapter 4
(2) Chapter 2   (4) Chapter 6

Compare and Contrast

Read the passage and compare the following types of honeybees.

Lee el pasaje y compara los tipos siguientes de abejas.

Although there are about 20,000 kinds of bees in the world, honeybees are the most useful to people. They produce honey, which people use as food. They also produce beeswax, a substance that is used to make candles, crayons, and makeup.

Honeybees are social bees that live in groups called colonies inside hives. A hive might be a box or a hollow tree. The central structure of the colony is the wax comb, which is made up of six-sided, white wax chambers, or rooms. Some honeybee colonies have as many as 80,000 members. There are usually three types of bees in a colony—a queen, workers, and drones—and each type has a specific role to perform.

The queen's only job is to lay eggs. In the spring, the queen lays about 2,000 eggs a day! Each colony has only one queen, who may live for up to five years. If the old queen disappears or becomes feeble, a new queen is made. Sometimes a young queen fights with an old queen until one stings the other to death.

A drone's job is to mate with the queen. There can be up to 500 drones in each colony. Drones are not able to hunt for food because their tongues are too short to suck up nectar from flowers. So they depend on worker bees to feed them. Drones live in the hive in the summer, but in the winter, worker bees may kick them out of the hive if there is not enough food.

Worker bees neither lay eggs nor mate. They spend their entire lives performing duties, or jobs. There are thousands of workers in a colony. At the beginning of their lives, workers clean the hive and feed other bees. Then they produce wax and build honeycomb cells. Later, they protect the hive and eventually hunt for food. Workers hunt for food by sucking up nectar from flowers with their long tongues. Back in the hive, workers put the nectar in an empty cell, where it changes into honey. A worker bee can live anywhere from six weeks to several months.

People thousands of years ago ate honey that they stole from hives. Today, farmers keep hives of bees and sell the honey. Beekeepers have learned to handle their bees carefully. They wear special clothing, including veils to protect their faces. Thanks to the busy lives of bees, we can enjoy the sweet taste of honey and the fresh scent of candles.

Types of Honeybees	Alike	Different
Queen/Drone		
Drone/Worker		
Worker/Queen		

Challenge Project for Week 5

Challenge: Do research on a labyrinth, or maze as we call it today, and build your own marble maze from common items around the house. The earliest labyrinth was designed as a prison, but today many toys and games are based on the concept of the maze and challenging mazes are often found in amusement parks.

Reto: Investiga los laberintos y construye uno de canicas usando cosas de la casa. El laberinto más antiguo fue diseñado como una prisión, pero hoy muchos juguetes y juegos son basados en el concepto de laberintos y laberintos desafiantes se encuentran en los parques de attraciones.

Directions: Do research on the Internet or at the library and read about labyrinths and mazes. Take notes so you can write a few paragraphs about the history and uses of mazes to accompany the maze you will build.

Instrucciones: Investiga en la red o en la biblioteca y lee sobre laberintos. Toma apuntes para que puedas escribir unos párrafos sobre la historia de los laberintos para acompañar el laberinto que construirás.

For the base of the maze use a box top (shoebox top or sturdy gift box top) or stiff poster board cut to size. The poster board or box top should be sturdy enough to hold the weight of the items you will be attaching to it without bending or collapsing.

Para la base del laberinto usa una tapa de caja (caja de zapatos o de regalo) o cartón grueso del tamaño apropiado. El cartón grueso o tapa de caja debe de ser firme para sostener el peso de las cosas que le pegarás sin plegar o derrumbarse.

Gather up such items as straws, empty thread spools, film canisters, paper towel rolls, pipe cleaners, popsicle sticks, medium to heavyweight construction paper, marbles, poster putty, string, yarn, sandpaper, bubble wrap, masking tape, glue sticks or glue gun, scissors or an exacto knife, a ruler marked with inches, and a timer or stop watch. Use your imagination and try to arrange your maze so your marble will have to travel through different events such as tubes, funnels, slides, pinwheels and in and out the sides of the box. Try to make your marble change directions at least 10 times as it runs through the maze.

Junta cosas como popotes, bobinas vacías, rollos de papel, limpiapipas, palos de paletas, cartulina, canicas, plastilina, cuerda, hilo, lija, plástico de burbujas, cinta adhesiva, pegamento, tijeras o una navaja, una regla marcada con pulgadas y un reloj. Usa tu imaginación y trata de arreglar tu laberinto para que tu canica tenga que viajar a través de eventos diferentes como tubos, embudos, resbaladillas, molinillos y dentro y afuera de los lados de la caja. Trata de hacer que tu canica cambie de dirección por lo menos 10 veces como vaya por el laberinto.

After building your maze, run your marble through it several times from slower to faster speeds. To go slower, tilt the maze only slightly but tilt the maze at a steeper angle to go faster. Write a report about what you learned about mazes and labyrinths and analyze the various times it took the marble to run the maze propped at different heights.

Después de construir tu laberinto, corre tu canica en él varias veces a velocidades lentas y más rápidas. Para ir más lento, ladea el laberinto un poco, pero ladéalo más angulado para ir más rápido. Escribe un reporte sobre lo que aprendiste acerca de laberintos y analiza los varios tiempos que tardó la canica en llegar al final con alturas diferentes.

Terrific!

Certificate of
Achievement

This is to certify that

_____

(Name)

did an awesome job completing all the
activity pages for Week 5.

Your hard work is really paying off!

_____

(Date)

Awesome!
Fabulous!

Proposition and Support

Write three reasons to support one of the ideas below. Circle the idea you choose.

Escribe tres razones para apoyar una de las ideas abajo. Encierra en un círculo la idea que eliges.

> *It is important to reduce class size to improve the schools.*
>
> *Protecting the environment benefits everyone.*

Reason #1: _____

_____

Reason #2: _____

_____

Reason #3: _____

_____

Fill out the graphic organizer below to plan a proposition-and-support text. You can choose one of the propositions above or create one of your own. You may need to do some research at the library or on the Internet to find support for your proposition.

Llena la gráfica organizadora abajo para planear un texto de proposición y apoyo. Puedes elegir una de las proposiciones arriba o crear una tú mismo. Quizás necesites hacer investigación en la biblioteca o en la red para encontrar apoyo para tu proposición.

Proposition:

Supporting Idea #1:	Supporting Idea #2:	Supporting Idea #3:

Conclusion: _____

After researching your proposition topic, write a proposition-and-support paragraph using the information from your graphic organizer.

Después de investigar tu tópico de proposición, escribe un párrafo de proposición y apoyo usando la información de tu gráfica organizadora.

_____

_____

_____

_____

_____

_____

_____

_____

Persuasive Solutions

Persuasive writing is writing with the intent to alter the reader's opinion about a subject. Writing a persuasive paper helps us to look at evidence, to state ideas more clearly, to consider the claims of the opposition fairly, and to justify our own positions or opinions. Choose a problem, propose a solution, and fill out the graphic organizer. You may need to do some research at the library or on the Internet about the problem you have selected. Write a persuasive piece about your problem and solution, using information from the graphic organizer.

La escritura persuasiva es escritura con el intento de alterar la opinión del lector sobre un tema. Escribiendo un ensayo persuasivo nos ayuda a examinar evidencia, declarar nuestras ideas con más claridad, considerar las declaraciones de la oposición más justamente y justificar nuestras propias posiciones u opiniones. Elige un problema, propón una solución y llena la gráfica organizadora. Quizá necesites hacer investigación en la biblioteca o en la red sobre el problema que hayas seleccionado. Escribe un escrito persuasivo sobre tu problema y solución, usando información de la gráfica organizadora.

1. State the problem:

    _____

    _____

2. Propose a solution:

    _____

    _____

3. Fill out the pros and cons chart below.

Pro #1			Con #1
Pro #2			Con #2
Pro #3			Con #3

4. Final Decision or Solution: _____

    _____

    _____

5. On a separate sheet of paper, write a persuasive essay on your chosen problem that uses the information you have included above.

Order of Operations

Solve expressions in this order: PEMDAS

1. Parentheses: Do these operations first.
2. Exponents: Find these values next.
3. Multiply and Divide: In order from left to right
4. Add and Subtract: In order from left to right

Resuelve las expresiones en este orden: PEMDSR

1. *Paréntesis: Haz estas operaciones primero.*
2. *Exponentes: Luego encuentra esto valores.*
3. *Multiplicar y Dividir: En orden del lado izquierdo al lado derecho.*
4. *Sumar y Restar: En orden del lado izquierdo al lado derecho.*

Solve these expressions. Be sure to follow the order of operations listed above. The first problem is done for you.

Resuelve cada uno de los siguientes problemas de ecuaciones. Asegúrate de seguir el orden de las operaciones enumeradas anteriormente. El primer problema ya está hecho.

1. $(100 \div 2) - (6 \times 8) =$

2. $(100 \div 2) - (6 \times 8) + 2 =$

3. $3 + 28 \div 7 =$

4. $3 (14 - 6) =$

5. $(82 \div 2 - 16) \div 5 =$

6. $(16 - 3) (18 \div 9) =$

7. $84 \div 12 \times 7 - 18 =$

8. $\dfrac{96 - 41}{66 \div 6} =$

9. $\dfrac{17 + 13}{19 - 13} =$

10. $2(4 + 5) - (6 \times 3) =$

11. $3(2 + 6) - 3 \times 5 =$

12. $(9 \div 3) + (4 \times 7) - (20 \div 5) =$

13. $[(10 \div 2) \times 3] - (2 \times 6) + 3 =$

14. $2[(8 - 5) + (4 + 2)] =$

15. $3[2(4 + 1) - 3 \times 2] =$

16. $4[2(4 \div 2)] - 3^2 =$

Using the Library and Dictionary

Read the questions. Look for the best answer for each question. Circle the letter of the correct answer.

Lee las preguntas. Busca la mejor respuesta para cada una. Encierra en un círculo la letra de la respuesta correcta.

A. If a dictionary page has kipper and kitten as guide words, which one of the following words would be on the same page?

    (A) kip
    (B) Kipling
    (C) kitchen
    (D) kitty

1. "Document" would be found on a dictionary page with which of these guide words?

    (A) divider – dobbin
    (B) docent – docket
    (C) doctrine – dogfight
    (D) doable – docent

2. To find the most information about the battles of the Boer War, you should look in …

    (F) a newspaper.
    (G) a magazine.
    (H) an almanac.
    (J) an encyclopedia.

3. Where should you look to find the best way to get to Disneyland in Anaheim, California?

    (A) an atlas
    (B) a globe
    (C) a road map
    (D) a world map

4. Which probably best shows the geography of the states along the Mississippi?

    (F) a road map
    (G) a travel guide
    (H) an atlas
    (J) a globe

B. Where should you look for information about the government of France?

    (F) an atlas
    (G) an encyclopedia
    (H) an almanac
    (J) a travel guidebook

For items 5 and 6, find the answers by using this library catalog card.

629.1 **Interplanetary Flight**

C597

Interplanetary Flight, by Arthur Clarke; illus. with photographs and diagrams by Maury Hendrickson and Alice Bentley; New York: Jay Harper and Brothers, 1953

224 pages; illustrated

  1. Space exploration   2. Science

---

5. The book is about . . .

    (A) space exploration.
    (B) Arthur Clarke.
    (C) New York.
    (D) Jay Harper and Brothers.

6. Who is the author of the book?

    (F) Maury Hendrickson
    (G) Alice Bentley
    (H) Jay Harper
    (J) Arthur Clarke

Working with Circle Graphs

This circle graph illustrates which elements are most abundant in the earth's crust.

Esta gráfica de círculo ilustra los elementos que son más abundantes en la corteza de la tierra.

Use the circle graph to answer these questions.

Usa la gráfica de círculo para responder a estas preguntas.

1. Which is the most abundant element in the earth's crust? _____

2. Which two elements make up three-fourth's of the earth's crust? _____

   _____

3. Which two elements together are equal to the amount of aluminum in the earth's crust?

   _____

4. Where would carbon, hydrogen, and sodium be included? _____

5. Which element makes up almost half of the earth's crust? _____

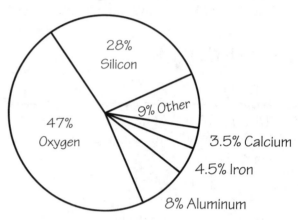

Elements as a Percentage of the Earth's Crust

28% Silicon
9% Other
47% Oxygen
3.5% Calcium
4.5% Iron
8% Aluminum

This circle graph illustrates the percentages of each major element in the human body.

Esta gráfica de círculo ilustra los porcentajes de cada elemento mayor en el cuerpo humano.

6. Which element makes up more than half of the human body? _____

7. How much higher is the percentage of carbon than the percentage of nitrogen? _____

8. What percentage of the human body do the three major elements total? _____

9. On the graph, where do you think copper, phosphorus, and iron are included?

   _____

10. What body compound would have much of the hydrogen and oxygen?_____

11. Why is this type of graph so easy to use?

   _____

   _____

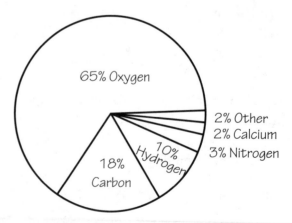

Major Elements as a Percentage of the Human Body

65% Oxygen
2% Other
2% Calcium
3% Nitrogen
10% Hydrogen
18% Carbon

Practicing Grammar

Read the words in each box. Then read each question below the box. Choose the best answers. Circle the letter of the correct answer.

Lee las palabras en cada caja. Luego lee cada pregunta abajo de la caja. Elige las mejores respuestas. Encierra en un círculo la letra de la respuesta correcta.

> I. Mr. Johnson is going to the football game.
>
> II. I am going to the football game.

A. Which of these words is used as an adjective in the sentences?
- (A)   going
- (B)   football
- (C)   game
- (D)   to

B. What is the subject of sentence I?
- (E)   Mr. Johnson
- (F)   is going
- (G)   game
- (H)   the football game

> I. Those bees have a hive in the maple tree.
>
> II. The bird has a nest in the maple tree.

1. Which word in these sentences is a preposition?
- (A)   those
- (B)   maple
- (C)   in
- (D)   the

2. What is the subject of sentence II?
- (E)   a nest
- (F)   bird has a nest
- (G)   the maple tree
- (H)   The bird

> I. The pencil is broken.
>
> II. The pencil was under your notebook.

3. Which of these words is used as a noun in the sentences?
- (A)   notebook
- (B)   under
- (C)   the
- (D)   broken

4. Which word in these sentences is a past tense verb?
- (E)   was
- (F)   is
- (G)   under
- (H)   broken

> I. The boys are at practice now.
>
> II. The boys were at practice on Friday.

5. Which word in these sentences is a present tense form of be?
- (A)   were
- (B)   at
- (C)   are
- (D)   on

6. Which of these words is used as an adverb in the sentences?
- (E)   practice
- (F)   were
- (G)   now
- (H)   Friday

Positive and Negative Numbers

There are times when you not only have no money at all, you may owe money to a parent or a friend. Negative numbers can be used to represent what you owe or how much you need just to get even. Negative numbers are also used in recording temperatures and golf games.

Hay veces cuando no sólo no tienes dinero, quizás también debas dinero a tus papás o a un amigo. Los números negativos se pueden usar para representar lo que debes o cuánto necesitas para quedar en cero. Los números negativos también se usan para registrar temperaturas y juegos de golf.

Apply your knowledge of integers (positive and negative numbers and zero) to help you solve these problems. Write an equation and then do the operations needed.

Aplica tu conocimiento de números enteros (números positivos, negativos y cero) para ayudarte a resolver estos problemas. Escribe una ecuación y luego haz las operaciones que necesites hacer.

1. You bought a watch for $12.00. Since you only had $2.00, you had to borrow money from your mom. What negative number shows what you owe?

   Equation: $+ 2 - 12 = -10$
   Answer: You owe $10.00.

2. The temperature when water freezes is 32°F. What temperature is 40° below freezing?

   Equation: _____
   Answer: _____

3. A golfer shot -4 (below par) on his first round of 18 holes. He shot an -11 on his second round and a -6 on his third round. How many shots below par was he after his three rounds?

   Equation: _____
   Answer: _____

4. The Acey Duecy Card Company owed the bank $1,000.00. They made a $750.00 payment to the bank. How much did they still owe the bank?

   Equation: _____
   Answer: _____

5. A player on a TV game show called *Double Trouble!* Had -600 points because of some hard questions. He then answered several questions correctly. He received 200 points, 100 points, and 150 points. How many points did the player have? How many points did he need to get to 0?

   Equation: _____
   Answer: _____

6. One of the coldest temperatures ever recorded was -69°F in Utah in 1985. What temperature is 35° higher than -69° F?

   Equation: _____
   Answer: _____

7. The coldest temperature ever recorded was -129°F in Antarctica. The highest recorded temperature was 136°F in Africa. What is the difference?

   Equation: _____
   Answer: _____

8. A temperature of -80°F was recorded in Alaska. What is the difference between this reading and a high of 134°F recorded in Death Valley, California?

   Equation: _____
   Answer: _____

Summarizing and Paraphrasing

Read the selection below and answer the five Ws.

Lee la selección abajo y contesta las cinco "Ws".

In 1613, the emperor of India, Shah Jahan was very unhappy. His beloved wife, Mumtaz Mahal, had died. Shah Jahan decided to build a tomb in his wife's memory. The tomb has become one of the most famous tourist sites in India. It is called the Taj Mahal, meaning "Crown of the Palace."

During their life together, the couple had fourteen children. Mumtaz often went with her husband on military journeys. When Mumtaz died, Shah Jahan was grief-stricken. Legend says that his hair turned white overnight. Mumtaz had asked her husband to make a promise before she died. She asked him to build a tribute to their eternal love. She also asked that he visit the tomb every year on the anniversary of her death. Shah Jahan honored these promises.

Agra is a city in north central India. Work on the tomb began in 1632. It took more than twenty years to build. Shah Jahan hired 20,000 men to construct the palace-like tomb. The building is made of white marble and sits on a base of red sandstone. The supplies needed to build the tomb came from all over India. They were brought to the area by 1,000 elephants.

There are tall towers, called minarets, standing 133 feet tall at each corner of the building. The minarets tilt slightly away from the building. This is so they will not fall on the tomb in the event of an earthquake. A huge dome was constructed over the center of the building. Precious stones were placed into the walls. They make the tomb sparkle at different times of the day. A special style of writing called calligraphy decorates the walls of the tomb. A long water pool was built outside the building and lined with trees and flowers. At certain times of the day, the beautiful Taj Mahal is reflected in the pool. The colors of the tomb change. They are pinkish in the morning, white in the evening, and golden colors when the moon shines. Sadly, the architect of the Taj Mahal was not rewarded well for his work. Stories say that Shah Jahan ordered all his fingers crushed to prevent him from ever designing a more beautiful building!

Today, the bodies of Shah Jahan and his wife lie beside one another in this monument to love. Some call the Taj Mahal the eighth wonder of the world.

1. **Who** ordered the Taj Mahal built? _____

2. **What** materials were used? _____

3. **Where** does it stand today? _____

4. **When** was construction begun and when was it completed? _____

5. **Why** was is built? _____

On a separate sheet of paper, write a summary of the reading selection using your answers.

En un hoja aparte, escribe un resumen de la selección de lectura usando tus respuestas.

Understanding Poetry

Read the following poem. Apply the reading strategy below to help you understand the poem better.

Lee el poema siguiente. Aplica la estrategia de lectura abajo para ayudarte a entender mejor el poema.

His Story

History lacks herstory
The essential fault is in
The pronoun

Kings, lords, warriors and knights, even
Explorers: all males
(some wearing mail,
some setting sail aboard ships named after females.)

His-story lacks her-story
We-males need
Fe-males.
Prince Henry, Edward the First
Alex the Great, Peter the Worst
Where are the daughters?
Do we ignore the wives?
Just X's on record—
So are there no Y's?

Please rewind
research
review
And relearn

Both sides of OUR-story
Give females their turn.

Listen: Listen to the rhythm of the poem as you read it.

Look: What images come to mind when you read this poem? _____

_____

Feel: How does the poem make you feel? _____

_____

Look again: Read each word one by one. Are there any hidden meanings? _____

What are they? _____

What is the importance of the title? _____

Listen again: What is the poet saying? What is the message? _____

_____

Similarities

A *simile* is a technique for comparing two things. Similes use the words *like* or *as* to show how the items are alike. Here are some similes.

Un símil es una técnica para comparar dos cosas. Los símiles usan las palabras "like" o "as" para mostrar cómo las cosas se parecen. He aquí algunos símiles.

> *Her teeth are as white as winter snow.* (Her teeth are white and snow is white.)
>
> *The snake was like a garden hose.* (The snake was thin and black and lying in the grass. The garden hose was also thin and black and lying in the grass.)

Explain the comparisons in the following similes:

Explica las comparaciones en los símiles siguientes:

1. The baby's cheeks are like a rose.

   The baby's cheeks are _____ and a rose is _____.

2. The full moon is like a cookie.

   The full moon is _____ and a cookie is _____.

3. The baseball whizzed by like a bullet.

   The baseball is _____ and a bullet is _____.

4. The coffee is like ink.

   Coffee is _____ and ink is _____.

Now you try it. Write some similes of your own.

Ahora hazlo tú. Escribe algunos símiles tuyos.

1. The boat is _____
   _____.

2. The cave is _____
   _____.

3. Her hair is _____
   _____.

Read your similes to a friend or family member. See if he or she can explain your comparisons.

Lee tus símiles a un amigo o miembro de familia. Ve si puede explicar tu comparaciones.

Challenge Project for Week 6

Challenge: Write a book about yourself. Your book should include a front and back cover, a table of contents, chapter titles and subheadings, pictures, drawings, maps, and other items that you want to include.

Reto: Escribe un libro sobre ti. Tu libro debe incluir una portada de frente y de fondo, una tabla de contenido, títulos de capítulos y subtítulos, fotografías, dibujos, mapas y otras cosas que quieras incluir.

Your book should include the following chapters:

Tu libro debe incluir los capítulos siguientes:

1. My Family—Include a separate page for mothers, fathers, sisters, and brothers. Put a picture of each family member on the page (you can use a photo or draw a picture) and underneath the picture, write one or two paragraphs about each person.

1. *Mi familia—Incluye una página separada para madres, padres, hermanas y hermanos. Pon una fotografía de cada miembro de tu familia en la página (puedes usar una foto o hacer un dibujo) y debajo de la foto, escribe uno o dos párrafos acerca de cada persona.*

2. My Neighborhood—Draw a map of your neighborhood or take a picture of it. Write one or two paragraphs about your neighborhood. Describe it—what is it like?

2. *Mi vecindario—Dibuja un mapa de tu vecindario o toma una foto. Escribe uno o dos párrafos acerca de tu vecindario. Descríbelo—¿cómo es?*

3. My City—Do some reading about your city and write a travel article about it. What do you like about living in your city?

3. *Mi ciudad—Lee sobre tu ciudad y escribe un artículo de viaje describiéndola. ¿Por qué te gusta vivir en tu ciudad?*

4. My Projects—Include samples of your writing or artwork, such as poems, stories, pictures, essays, etc., that you have completed during these six weeks, as well as new ones you may want to do or others that you have on hand.

4. *Mis proyectos—Incluye muestras de tu escritura o arte, como poemas, historias, fotos, ensayos, etc., que has hecho durante estas seis semanas y también proyectos nuevos que quieres hacer u otros que tienes.*

5. My Favorite Things—Write about your favorite things. You can include a page for each one of your favorite things, such as your favorite food, favorite book, favorite television show, favorite sport, favorite colors, etc. This chapter should be all about you and what you like. Include pictures or photos.

5. *Mis cosas favoritas—Escribe sobre tus cosas favoritas. Puedes incluir una página para cada una de tus cosas favoritas, como tu comida favorita, libro favorito, programa de televisión favorito, deporte favorito, colores favoritos, etc. Este capítulo debe ser acerca de ti y lo que te gusta. Incluye fotos o dibujos.*

Outstanding! Terrific! Super Fantastic!

This certifies that

_____

(Name)

has done outstanding work
on the activity pages
for Week 6.

Thank you
for your
dedication!

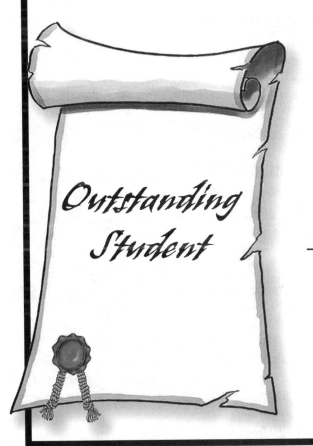

Outstanding Student

_____

(Parent)

_____

(Date)

Useful Vocabulary Words

Here is a list of some vocabulary words that you might find useful when reading and writing. Make a set of vocabulary flashcards by looking up the definition of each word in a dictionary. Then try using them in practice sentences or in a short paragraph.

He aquí una lista de unas palabras de vocabulario que quizás encontrarás útil cuando leas y escribas. Haz un juego de tarjetas de vocabulario al buscar la definición de cada palabra usando un diccionario. Luego trata de usarlas en oraciones de práctica o en un párrafo corto.

- accessory
- accommodate
- adapt
- affect
- aggressive
- although
- analysis
- ancestor
- appropriate
- authentic
- avert
- bacteria
- basis
- behavior
- biodegradable
- brake
- break
- brilliant
- calculate
- candor

- cellular
- challenge
- characteristic
- chronological
- concur
- comprehensive
- conspicuous
- continuous
- contaminant
- creak
- creek
- curious
- days
- daze
- decimal
- debacle
- declaim
- demographics
- dismiss
- distress

Useful Vocabulary Words *(cont.)*

- doubtful
- duplicate
- edible
- editorial
- effect
- eloquent
- emissions
- emphatic
- enthusiasm
- estimate
- evidence
- evoke
- exception
- factor
- feat
- ferocious
- flour
- flourish
- flower
- foliage

- forth
- fossil
- foul
- fourth
- fowl
- fragile
- frequent
- friction
- fundamental
- gait
- gate
- genetics
- genuine
- gesture
- gradual
- gravity
- growth
- gymnasium
- habitat
- harass

Useful Vocabulary Words *(cont.)*

- hearty
- height
- hesitate
- hilarious
- however
- humanity
- hybrid
- hydrogen
- icon
- identify
- idle
- idol
- illusion
- imagination
- implausible
- impress
- incredulous
- inference
- introduction
- irresistible

- judgment
- justice
- juvenile
- laboratory
- lavish
- liberty
- mainstream
- margin
- maximum
- meanwhile
- menial
- mere
- metaphor
- mysterious
- necessary
- negotiate
- neuron
- neutral
- objective
- obligation

Useful Vocabulary Words *(cont.)*

- often
- ought
- oxygen
- particle
- peer
- peril
- persuade
- physics
- placid
- pollution
- precede
- predict
- protagonist
- punctuate
- quantify
- quotation
- recur
- regimen
- require
- resource

- retrieve
- revere
- revise
- scarce
- scientific
- sequence
- similarity
- simile
- species
- symbol
- synthetic
- technology
- thoughtful
- thrive
- throughout
- unusual
- urban
- which
- witch
- youth

One-Inch Graph Paper

Tear out this page and use it for the Challenge Activity on page 66.

Corta esta hoja y úsala para el proyecto de desafió de la pagina 66.

Writing Paper

Writing Paper

Writing Paper

Writing Paper